PRESS

5 PLAYS for CHILDREN

BY BLANCHE MARVIN

FIREBIRD
Japanese Noh Style

PIED PIPER
Elizabethan Classical Style

THE BIRTHDAY OF THE INFANTA
Spanish Classical Style

THE LEGEND OF SCARFACE AND BLUEWATER
Naturalistic Style
performed by children

PRINTED BY O'REILLY CLARK PRINTING SERVICES
32 RUSSELL ROAD, ENFIELD EN1 4TY
TELEPHONE: 081-367 9603

FOREWORD

The three fairy tales, The Firebird, The Pied Piper, and the Birthday of the Infanta are each carefully chosen to suit the style of theatre appropriate to the story. Familiar fairy tales become a subliminal way of acquainting children with the application of style in theatre, not just from the writing but from the source of the material itself. It is organic rather than imposed.

The Firebird, the Birthday of the Infanta and The Pied Piper are plays for actors to perform for children's audiences, age 2 to 70.

A production breakdown with the scenic, costume and make-up plots is included for school and amateur groups. Professional theatre companies might also find them useful. But whether professional or amateur productions, good acting and talented actors of young adult age are necessary.

So we have Japanese, English and Spanish settings - a variety of style and place. The casts are small, with single sets adaptable to the many scenes, costumes that are decorative but one costume per actor, musical selections on tape, all making a repertoire possible for schools, theatre and touring. These plays are easy to produce for puppets and animation.

FIREBIRD

by BLANCHE MARVIN

THE FIREBIRD

Empress Chun

Prince Sunang

Prince Moatang

Prince Hoasang

The Firebird

Stage Manager

Pui-sing, the Cook

Place: Garden of the Empress Chun's Palace in Japan con-
            taining the sacred statue of Buddha.

Time: Long ago.

The Firebird is to be produced as a Japanese Noh play, all of
its movement choreographed in order to stylise the piece. The
fans are used to heighten speech and are therefore part of
the choreography. Movement is important in all plays as they
are a form of communication easily understood by children, but
particularly so in The Firebird as all the movement is co-
ordinated with the text. The Japanese Noh plays always have
the same theme, no matter the change of story - love and
happiness are ephemeral and cannot be captured.

Since The Firebird must not be captured or she would die it was
a perfect fairy tale for the Noh style. The setting in Japan
enhances the story and the exotic make-up and costumes, the
sword fights, the set of six screens fascinate children.

Benjamin Britten's Japanese Suite is the right key for the
music. The songs emanate from the plot, but the background
music should give fluidity to the piece as with the movement. A
sense of mystery pervades and its resolution has deep moral
fulfillment, love is letting go and not possessing. It is a force
that lives on while evil destroys itself.

Pictures and programmes are indexed in the back of the book.

ACT ONE

AS THE HOUSE LIGHTS DIM, A MAN DRESSED IN A JAPANESE STYLE COSTUME COMES OUT IN FRONT OF THE JAPANESE SCREENS WHICH FRONT THE SET AND ADDRESSES THE AUDIENCE. HE IS THE STAGE MANAGER.

STAGE MANAGER
Honourable children on such an honourable day
We sit to behold an honourable play.

(THROWS GOLD AND RED PAPER INTO AIR. MUSIC)

It is the tale of a bird who lived in a land
Where an Empress ruled with an iron hand.

(HAND MOTIONS MIME STORY AS HE SPEAKS)

She had three sons and the youngest of three
Was the one she loved most ardently.

The eldest was to rule the land
But the Empress sought for his golden hand
That he could not give
For he knew not how.
And that is where
I make my bow.

MUSIC ENDS. HE CLAPS HIS HANDS THREE TIMES IN FRONT OF THE SCREENS WHICH THEN OPEN FROM CENTRE TO FORM THREE LEGS ON STAGE RIGHT AND LEFT AND WE ARE IN THE GARDEN OF THE PALACE OF THE GREAT EMPRESS CHUNG. WE SEE A BUDDHA AND SIMPLE ORIENTAL SCENERY. TWO PRINCES ARE DISCOVERED MOTIONLESS. PRINCE SUNANG IS SOFT AND PETULANT. MOATANG IS CUNNING AND RUTHLESS. HE CLAPS AGAIN AND THE PRINCES BEGIN PACING. EVERY ONCE IN A WHILE THEY STOP, LOOK AT EACH OTHER, AND THEN GO ON PACING. THE SCENE BEGINS SLOWLY IN A FORMALIZED MANNER AND BUILDS TO ITS CLIMAX IN THE SWORD-FIGHT.

MOATANG Brother, you speak first - you are the elder.

SUNANG I cannot. I am too angered. If I speak now - I will say terrible things.

MOATANG Such as -

SUNANG (STOPS PACING) Such as - since I am the eldest son - our mother Her Royal Empress - should give me my royal due. Instead she gives everything to Hoasang.

MOATANG My thoughts are with yours. He is the youngest son and should have fewer favours. But he is the Empress's favourite.

BOTH RESUME THEIR STYLIZED PACING.

9

MOATANG I – excuse me, brother – you want me to say something. It is your privilege to speak first.

SUNANG Thank you, Moatang. We must do something with Hoasang.

MOATANG We must indeed. I have been thinking it over and over.

SUNANG What are your thoughts, brother?

MOATANG We must make the Empress send him away – for learning some new ideas.

SUNANG That will never happen.

MOATANG Then we must convince Hoasang first.

THEIR PACING RESUMES. AN IDEA STRIKES PRINCE MOATANG. THEY BOTH STOP, EXTEND THEIR ARMS AND WALK TOWARD EACH OTHER. AFTER SHAKING HANDS, THEY SMILE GRADUALLY. THEIR SMILES BROADEN TO HUGE GRINS. EACH HAS HIS OWN SOLUTION.

SUNANG We must tempt him with gold and silver!

MOATANG He wishes for none of that. Besides the Empress would never allow him to leave, even if he should want to go.

SUNANG (HIS IDEA LOST) Something must be done.

MOATANG It will be – by the sword! (HE TAKES OUT HIS SWORD IN FRIGHTFUL ANGER)

SUNANG (FEARFUL OF HIS BROTHER AND HIS TEMPER) Do not be a fool. We should neither of us live to rule.

MOATANG Neither of us – was it not agreed that we should both rule together.

SUNANG (FIGHTING BACK) Moatang – I will one day be the rightful Emperor – but will share the empire with you.

MOATANG We will both be Emperor – it was agreed.

SUNANG It was agreed that I would share my place with you.

MOATANG (COMPLETELY LOSING CONTROL) Lies – lies – lies – defend your place! Fight for being Emperor.

HE DRAWS HIS SWORD AND FORCES PRINCE SUNANG TO DRAW HIS.

SUNANG Fool – fool – that we should quarrel.

MOATANG Take care, or there will be one less brother.

SUNANG   Maybe you will understand my sword better.

> MUSIC. SWORD FIGHT DANCE. THEY REALLY DUEL. IN THE MIDST OF THIS HEATED BATTLE THE DOWAGER EMPRESS ARRIVES, A STERN WOMAN WITH STEEL STRENGTH AND WARM HEART. SHE STANDS STILL - OPENS HER GOLDEN FAN OF AUTHORITY. CLEARLY SHE IS ANGERED.

EMPRESS   Enough. Enough I say. Is this how two brothers love one another?

SUNANG   I defended my birth right.

EMPRESS   (CONTROLLING HER ANGER) It would need no defending if you were worthy of it.

SUNANG   And why am I not worthy of it?

EMPRESS   Where is your heart - what is it that you love? You may not rule without my consent - and my consent will be given when you are worthy of love.

SUNANG   (SARCASTICALLY) What is it that I should love?

EMPRESS   If you do not know that now then no words of mine can tell you.

MOATANG   Where is the love for your eldest sons - you ask for love - but do you give it?

EMPRESS   Moatang, yours is the bitter tongue, son of mine though you are. Love is not given - only earned. When you were a babe and too young to know I gave you all my love. Now as a man you must earn it from me - as I from you.

MOATANG   Who is to judge the earning of it? You look only to Hoasang.

EMPRESS   I look to where it can be found. If I cannot teach you, there is someone who will. The great scholar, Taosung.

SUNANG   You would send us away?

EMPRESS   Yes - to the Province of Fituawana where you will be taught by the hands of a man. These hands are not strong enough.

MOATANG   And what of Hoasang?

EMPRESS   He shall remain. He is too young to go.

SUNANG   But we would help him.

EMPRESS   What you must learn - he has no need of.

MOATANG   (ANGERED) It is Hoasang who is your favourite.

EMPRESS (ANSWERING HIS ANGER WITH HER OWN) It is Sunang who should one day rule. He must learn and so must you.

MOATANG And what of Hoasang - I ask again?

EMPRESS He is still a boy - and when he is of age I shall send him too - if need be.

SUNANG Are there no scholars in our kingdom?

EMPRESS There are many - but none have the brilliance of Taosung.

MOATANG You wish only to be rid of us.

EMPRESS Royal Empress, I order you to pack your belongings and make ready for your journey.

MOATANG Where is the love you spoke of?

EMPRESS In the heart that sends you away.

> MUSIC FOR THEIR EXIT. STYLIZATION OF THE MOVEMENT STOPS - BUT MUST FLOW. THEY EXIT FILLED WITH HATE AND REVENGE.

STAGE MANAGER
Not as Empress - but as Mother go
Ask of Buddha what you wish to know.

EMPRESS (IN ANGUISH TO BUDDHA) Give me some of your wisdom - your peace. For I know there is some right on their side. What have I done wrong? How can I let either of them rule when they have an evil about them? They must learn your goodness first. (SHE MOVES ABOUT) Children are a problem. They must constantly be taught. Sometimes they are only half-wrong. Oh, what a decision.

> MUSIC.

VOICE OF BUDDHA Through my mossy years - in this garden - I have watched shadows of evening creeping on lengthy paws until they reach dawn. How many years have crept thusly. Shadows that bend with the wind - shadows of leaves on moving water - shadows of birds in flight - Firebirds - with colours of magic hue. Which is shadow - which is substance? Shadows of men - shadows of shadows. Where are the answers I have not yet found?

> END OF MUSIC.

EMPRESS Then how should I know any answers? Tell me -

> NO MORE IS HEARD. SHE WANDERS AWAY INTO THE GARDEN STILL INVOLVED IN HER OWN THOUGHTS. LIGHT GAY MUSIC CAN BE HEARD OFF STAGE. WE HEAR A FAINT SONG STILL OFF STAGE. THE STAGE MANAGER RE-ENTERS AND ARRANGES THE TREES. HE SPEAKS AS HE WORKS AND LISTENS TO THE SONG.

STAGE MANAGER
Hoasang is there
It's in the air.

OFF STAGE WE HEAR HOASANG'S SONG.

HOASANG
Catch a star
From afar
Bring it near
Startling clear.

STAGE MANAGER
The dark is light.
The trees have sight.

HOASANG
Catch a fish
Make a wish
Dreams come true
With evening dew.

STAGE MANAGER
The petals chatter
The leaves clatter

HOASANG
Catch the moon
On full bloom
Oh silvery beam
Where is my dream?

STAGE MANAGER
May joy surround
What I have found.

HOASANG APPEARS. HE IS YOUNG, WITH A TRUE JOY OF LIVING. HE HOLDS A BOUQUET OF CHERRY BLOSSOMS. HE SMELLS IT AND THEN LOVINGLY PUTS IT DOWN BY THE BUDDHA. DURING THIS CEREMONIAL DANCE, THE EMPRESS WANDERS BACK AND SEES HIM.

EMPRESS (WITH GREAT SADNESS) How my heart lightens to see you, oh light of my life.

HOASANG (TURNING AROUND) Mother, why do you cry out in such pain?

EMPRESS I have always loved you. And once I did love my two eldest.

HOASANG Do you not love them now?

MEANWHILE THE TWO BROTHERS HAVE STOLEN IN WITHOUT BEING SEEN. THEIR PURPOSE IS TO KILL HOASANG. THEY OVERHEAR THE SCENE BETWEEN THEIR MOTHER AND BROTHER.

EMPRESS It is one thing to love an innocent baby and another to respect a man.

HOASANG   What have they done?

EMPRESS   They are filled with hate, and so I will send them away.

HOASANG   From the Palace?

EMPRESS   Yes.

EMPRESS   Where are they now? I must go to them.

EMPRESS   Packing in their chambers.

HOASANG   They are not there. I have looked and looked all evening.

EMPRESS   Then we must find them.

HOASANG   What makes you so fearful?

EMPRESS   The time is drawing near for a son to become Emperor. If your brothers remain as they are, you shall be the heir to the throne. They know this. I fear they are plotting - somewhere.

HOASANG   Oh my mother, abandon such unworthy thoughts. Let us find my brothers and tell them that I have no right to the throne.

UPON THESE WORDS THE BROTHERS, IN TRYING TO ATTACK HOASANG FROM BEHIND, BETRAY THEIR PRESENCE AND ARE FORCED TO ABANDON HIS MURDER. THEY PANIC AT BEING DIS-COVERED. AT FIRST THEY TRY TO HIDE THEIR SWORDS BUT THEY SOON GIVE UP AND STAND STILL WITH EYES DOWNCAST.

EMPRESS   Behold yourselves. How shall a new Emperor be chosen from one of you when there is murder in your hearts. Delay no further. You leave tonight.

BEFORE THEY CAN ANSWER, THE COOK COMES RUNNING IN. SHE IS OBLIVIOUS TO ALL ABOUT HER. A FEY WOMAN, YET WITH GREAT DETERMINATION. SHE IS DISTURBED.

COOK   How can they say there are no more cherries in the garden? I shall look for myself. (SHE GOES ABOUT SEARCHING)

EMPRESS   (ANGERED) Piu-sing! Piu-sing!

COOK   Someone calls me.

EMPRESS   Piu-sing, your Empress addresses you.

COOK   Oh your majesty, forgive me.

SHE DROPS TO HER KNEES BEFORE THE EMPRESS.

EMPRESS   You must leave the gardens at once.

COOK   Oh your majesty, I had no idea that I was disturbing...

EMPRESS   Piu-sing, up at once and leave us in peace.

COOK   Peace - your majesty - when there is black magic at work.

> EVERYONE REACTS WITH FEAR - IN STYLIZED MOVEMENT WITH USE OF HANDS.

EMPRESS   (DRAWING CLOSER)   What say you?

COOK   I say there is black magic - in this very garden -

EMPRESS   What has happened that we do not know?

COOK   (IN A TRANCE)   The cherries have been destroyed - eaten in every garden in the whole kingdom - even in ours.

EMPRESS   Tell the gardener to plant more.

COOK   It does no good. Slowly the cherry trees are being killed. No more blossoms, no more fruit. Where is the scent of our blossoms that smothered the land in beauty? Where great Empress?   (FALLS TO HER KNEES)

EMPRESS   Oh Buddha - have you sent us a warning?

COOK   What great evil have we done?

EMPRESS   Is there an evil spirit in this Garden?

COOK   There is - there is. Some say it is a demon - fiery red with winged feet and winged arms. Others say it is a bird, a strange and beautiful bird, who devours the fruit of our land.

EMPRESS   Silence! If this be a warning to me, Buddha, if you are testing my strength then I am willing. I have three sons. They shall remain. Whoever finds and captures this evil spirit will become Emperor.

SUNANG   But mother, my place cannot be given away.

EMPRESS   It shall not be given away. If you are worthy of it - you shall win. As my eldest, you have the right to try first.

SUNANG   As you will.

EMPRESS   My sons, make your plans, and may the best Prince become Emperor. (SHE POINTS TO EACH ONE DURING THIS SPEECH)

> MUSIC. THE THREE SONS ARE TOGETHER, LOOKING BEWILDER-
> ED. THE STAGE MANAGER CLOSES THE SCREENS.
> END OF ACT ONE.

ACT TWO

THE STAGE MANAGER APPEARS BEFORE THE SCREENS AND ADDRESSES THE AUDIENCE.

STAGE MANAGER
It is late at night.
The birds in flight
Have found their rest
Within their nest.
Sunang remains
As darkness gains.

HE OPENS THE SCREENS. MUSIC. THE SCENE AS FOR ACT ONE ONLY NOW IT IS EVEN DARKER. SUNANG IS WALKING STEALTH-ILY ABOUT. EACH TIME HE THINKS HE HEARS SOMETHING HE STOPS PETRIFIED. HE LISTENS THEN RESUMES HIS WALK. MEANTIME MOATANG HAS SECRETLY CREPT OUT AND KEEPS WALKING ABOUT FOLLOWING SUNANG'S SHADOW. EVERY TIME SUNANG STOPS, MOATANG HIDES. THEN BOTH HIDE AND AS THEY COME OUT OF HIDING BACK TO BACK LOOKING IN OPP-OSITE DIRECTIONS THEY BUMP INTO EACH OTHER. EACH JUMPS AWAY FROM THE OTHER. MUSIC ENDS.

SUNANG & MOATANG Who's that?

THEY TURN SLOWLY TOWARD EACH OTHER DRAWING SWORDS.

SUNANG   Oh! It's you - my brother. I'm glad to see you.

MOATANG   (FEIGNING GLADNESS) I too am glad it is you.

SUNANG   What are you doing here?

MOATANG   (INGRATIATING) I came to help you.

SUNANG   Thank you. (SUSPICIOUS) Have you seen anything?

SUNANG   (WITH A STYLIZED MOVEMENT OF FATIGUE) It is almost dawn and no one has appeared.

MOATANG   (HYPOCRITICALLY) Why don't you rest. I'll stand watch for you.

SUNANG   (STARTS TO REST AND SUDDENLY RISES) What if some-thing should appear?

MOATANG   I'll wake you.

SUNANG   Remember it is my turn.

MOATANG   Of course, brother, go rest.

PRINCE SUNANG QUITE CONFIDENTLY LIES DOWN AND INSTANTLY FALLS ASLEEP.

MOATANG If something should appear, I shall capture it. Then the kingdom will be mine.

> HE IS VERY PLEASED WITH HIMSELF. BUT AFTER A WHILE FATIGUE OVERCOMES HIM AND HE TOO LIES DOWN AND FALLS ASLEEP. THE STAGE MANAGER MOVES OVER THEM AS IF TO MAKE SURE THEY ARE SLEEPING.

STAGE MANAGER
In its bright red cloak
The dawn gently broke
And with it had come
The Bird of the Sun.

> SUDDENLY THE FIREBIRD ENTERS. SHE DANCES AROUND THE GARDEN PLUCKING THE TREES. SHE CREATES THE AURA OF OVERWHELMING BEAUTY. AS THE SUN RISES THE DANCE ENDS AND SHE DISAPPEARS.

STAGE MANAGER
The spirit they sought
Would never be brought
To the Empress's court.
Oh Brothers distraught
What will you report?

> CLAPS HIS HANDS. THE PRINCES AWAKEN.

SUNANG (IN A FURY) You fell asleep! I have lost my kingdom.

MOATANG But brother, I was awake until the dawn and no one came.

SUNANG You have lost your turn for your carelessness.

MOATANG My turn is tonight. I only came to help you.

SUNANG Help me - by falling asleep! You have tricked me. (HE GOES TOWARD HIM MENACINGLY)

MOATANG (STANDS HIS GROUND) No, my brother, you must believe in my good faith.

SUNANG Your good faith! I thought fear would keep us together. I shall believe you only if you relinquish your turn.

MOATANG (PLACATING SUNANG) I promise to do so. (TO HIMSELF) My turn will come when both my brothers are defeated!
(TO SUNANG) What shall we do about Hoasang?

SUNANG He must fail too.

MOATANG But how?

SUNANG You think of an answer.

MOATANG He too must fall asleep – some way.

SUNANG And by what means?

MOATANG I have it! We shall put a sleeping potion in his drink and give it to him while he stands guard.

SUNANG An excellent idea.

A GONG IS HEARD. MUSIC FOLLOWS.

MOATANG Quickly now, the Empress is arriving. Remember, we saw nothing.

SUNANG Nothing – nothing at all.

EMPRESS Ah Sunang – and Moatang – what news have you for me?

SUNANG We stood watch together and yet with our four eyes we saw nothing.

EMPRESS Impossible! Someone or something has been in the garden. There is magic at work. You have both failed.

SUNANG Let Hoasang try tonight.

EMPRESS Indeed he shall.

SUNANG We are very tired, Mother, after being up all night. May we retire?

EMPRESS Of course, my sons.

(THEY EXIT. THE EMPRESS IS SADDENED – DEFEATED. WE SEE HER FOR THE SECOND TIME AS MOTHER. SHE SINGS. MUSIC)

I have three sons
And the youngest of three
Is the one I love
Most ardently.

Hoasang is his name
And for him is my plea
Hoasang, my son
Do NOT fail me.

Evil spirit wherever you are
Do not dim my young one's star
For he is the greatest Prince by far.

I will do, Buddha, as you will say
Only give Hoasang the winning day.

I have three sons
And the youngest of three
Is the one I love
Most ardently.

Hoasang is his name
And for him is my plea
Hoasang my son
DO – NOT – FAIL – ME!
Do not fail me
Do not fail me.

EXIT. SLOW FADE-OUT.

SCENE TWO

THE STAGE MANAGER RE-APPEARS BEFORE THE ALREADY OPENED SCREENS.

STAGE MANAGER
And now Hoasang stood alone
To find the secret writ on stone
The evil spirit must appear
For him to touch, to see, to hear.

IT IS NOW THE EVENING OF THE SAME DAY. HOASANG SITS ALONE IN THE GARDEN, IN A BLUE LIGHT.

HOASANG (TO THE CHILDREN IN THE AUDIENCE) Mother really believes in such a thing as magic, and that it will be here in this garden. My poor brothers have failed. They will never be able to please her. How will they learn to love one another? Should I discover any magic at work here tonight, Mother will make me King and then what will become of Sunang who is the rightful heir? If this magic could only help us all.

THE TWO PRINCES APPEAR WITH A TRAY AND THREE GLASSES OF WINE.

SUNANG   There you are Hoasang! Come join us in the last of the cherry wine.

MOATANG Rather suitable for the occasion, don't you think?

SUNANG SECRETLY DROPS SOME POWDER IN THE MIDDLE GLASS THEN GIVES IT TO HOASANG.

SUNANG   This is yours, Hoasang. This is yours, Moatang. And the last mine.

MOATANG A toast.

HOASANG (SUDDENLY, BUT PLAYFULLY) Put your glasses down quickly.

SUNANG   What is it?

HOASANG AND THE OTHERS PUT THEIR GLASSES ON THE TABLE. HOASANG PROCEEDS TO MIX THEM AROUND CONCENTRATING VERY CAREFULLY ON SOMETHING AS HE DOES.

MOATANG Does he know?

SUNANG I don't know. (THEY WATCH FEARFULLY) What are you doing?

HOASANG (MYSTERIOUSLY – AS IF PLAYING THE PART OF A MAGICIAN) Now look. I turn the glasses upside down – the wine is gone. One – two – three – no more.

MOATANG (FURIOUS) Hoasang, it was the last of the cherry wine. Heaven knows when we shall ever taste any more.

HOASANG Oh, forgive me, Moatang, but the spirit of magic moved me and I did so want to show you my new trick. (TO SUNANG) This waiting for something to happen is frightening.

MOATANG As long as you made the wine disappear, now make it reappear.

SUNANG (FRIGHTENED) I think not.

MOATANG Why not?

SUNANG (WHISPERING TO MOATANG) Who knows where it has been?

HOASANG I forgot the rest of the trick.

MOATANG Very well.

SUNANG (THINKING SOMETHING UP) Can we help you tonight?

HOASANG No, thank you, Sunang.

> THE PRINCES SUNANG AND MOATANG START TO LEAVE BUT THEN THEY NOTICE THE COOK WHO HAS ENTERED THE GARDEN AND IS LOOKING BEHIND THE TREES IN QUIET SEARCH OF SOMETHING.

HOASANG (AS PRINCE) Piu-sing, why are you here in the garden?

COOK (JUMPING IN FEAR) Oh! To see if the evil spirit is about.

HOASANG It is forbidden for you to enter.

COOK But someone or something has stolen the last of the cherry wine. And here is the missing jug.

HOASANG Leave it be.

COOK Oh I must find out if the evil spirit drank it.

MOATANG No spirit was about.

COOK Then where did the wine go to?

SUNANG Why are you so concerned with the wine?

COOK   (TEARFULLY) Because I put poison in it - to kill the evil
spirit.

THEY ALL REACT.

MOATANG   You - put - poison -

SUNANG   If not for your magic trick, Hoasang, we would all...

HOASANG   Brothers, it was not meant for us to drink the cherry
wine.

COOK   No, never. You didn't - oh, what have I done?

MOATANG   Nothing. We never touched the wine.

SUNANG   Moatang, I think it is time to go.

PIU-SING PICKS UP WINE JUG AS THE BROTHERS START TO
LEAVE.

HOASANG   Brothers, be not afraid. Should I succeed I will share
my success with you.

THE BROTHERS NOD AND LEAVE DEFEATED.

STAGE MANAGER
Alone Hoasang must sit and wait
Whilst no one can his fear abate
Be there a spirit or be there none
He must find the answers for everyone. (CLAPS)

MUSIC.

HOASANG
Gardens of moonlight
Waving trees
Cast thy shadows
On the one who sees.
What wondrous delight
Without sound or sight
Will the uncovered secrets
Bring this night?

HE SITS QUIETLY AS THE DAWN GENTLY APPEARS AND WITH IT
THE FIREBIRD. SHE STARTS HER DANCE WHEN SUDDENLY SHE
SEES THE PRINCE. SHE STARTS TO FLY AWAY. HOASANG SEES
HER - TRIES TO CAPTURE HER BUT SHE FLIES AWAY.

Stay. Stay. I will not hurt you. Only stay. Come back, please.

SHE FLEES AS WE HEAR THE PRINCE CALLING HER BACK.

THE STAGE MANAGER APPEARS AND CLOSES THE SCREENS.

END OF ACT TWO

ACT THREE

THE STAGE MANAGER ENTERS AS BEFORE.

STAGE MANAGER
Hoasang beheld the bird so rare
Whose beauty stood beyond compare
And now must choose what's to be done
For love not evil was the uncaptured one.

> HE OPENS THE SCREENS. THE TWO PRINCES AND THE EMPRESS
> ARE ALL ENWRAPPED IN WHAT HOASANG IS SAYING.

HOASANG (TRANSFORMED) She was so beautiful - I cannot describe it. The red and gold of her feathers - her face of pure love. She danced about the garden with so much grace. But when she heard my voice she flew away.

EMPRESS (GREEDILY) I must have this bird, this thing of beauty. You must wait for her again tonight.

SUNANG   (FEARFUL) And what of the Kingdom?

EMPRESS   The Kingdom? Only if the bird is captured and brought to me, then will Hoasang inherit the Kingdom.

HOASANG   Mother, I wish only to please you, but what if I cannot capture the bird?

EMPRESS   Then you forfeit the Kingdom. I must have the bird.

> MUSIC.   THE EMPRESS EXITS.   THE TWO PRINCES WEAVE A
> PATTERNED MOVEMENT AROUND HOASANG CLOSER AND CLOSER.

SUNANG   So now you too lose the Empress's favour.

HOASANG   I want her love - not the Kingdom. But the bird was so frightened.

MOATANG   Unless you capture her, we'll not know she's real.

SUNANG   That's true. Mother will believe anything you say. But how do we know you didn't make this up?

HOASANG   I couldn't make up such a story.

SUNANG   For the Kingdom you might say anything.

HOASANG   But I don't want the Kingdom.

MOATANG   You had best bring the bird back and show us.

SUNANG   Until then, the Kingdom is mine.

> THEY EXIT LEAVING HOASANG ALONE.

STAGE MANAGER
Not as a Prince - but as a man
Now go
Ask of Buddha - what you wish to know.

HOASANG
What shall I do?
What shall I say?

STAGE MANAGER
Only Buddha will know the way.

HOASANG GOES TO THE BUDDHA.

BUDDHA
Life of the living - Life of shadows.
Wherein lies the good? Wherein lies the evil?
How does one know?
Weigh and balance. Weigh and balance.
You love the shadow of love - the Firebird.
Wait for her. She will come to you.

HOASANG But she will not stay when she sees me.

BUDDHA
The cherry blossoms blow
My message with the wind.

HOASANG Shall I capture her after such trust?

BUDDHA
Weigh and balance.
Weigh and balance.

HOASANG You are so much wiser than I and can make a choice.
But I am not sure.

BUDDHA
The choice is made
Only wait and see.

THE MUSIC STARTS AND THE FIREBIRD APPEARS, DANCING HER
DANCE FOR HOASANG.

HOASANG Oh lovely bird, why did you come to the Empress's
garden?

FIREBIRD They are the loveliest in the world.

HOASANG And what of the gardens in your Home?

FIREBIRD
They are gardens without trees
Brooks without water
Willows without weeping.

HOASANG Do you weep for your lost gardens?

FIREBIRD (DANCING OUT THE IMAGERY) No more. I weep no more. For I remember when the cherry blossoms bloomed in abundance and the petals danced with perfumed music. The gentle bridges partnered by the weeping willows whose tears turned to laughter by the babbling brook. Masked mountains - mountains of no faces stood in a ring forbidding strangers to enter. And I as Princess of that Realm loved all that loveliness even when I was captured by the Demons of Darkness. I must go.

HOASANG But now that I have seen you, I want you to stay.

> HOASANG CAPTURES HER. HE GENTLY HOLDS HER OUT OF LOVE. SHE IS TERRIFIED. SHE PLEADS FOR HER LIFE.

FIREBIRD Let me go. My home is southward where warm breezes blow. I must journey home.

HOASANG When winter comes you may stay in the Palace.

FIREBIRD Then I would perish. My wings would dry. Oh! listen to the wind and the music it makes. I must fly with it.

> HOASANG RELEASES HER. SHE IS CARRIED AWAY, DANCING TO THE MUSIC. HOASANG JOINS HER IN A DANCE OF LOVE AND HARMONY.

HOASANG I could dance my life away with you.

FIREBIRD (FLUTTERS HER WINGS IN TORMENT) But I am only a bird and you are a great Prince.

HOASANG Then I too will become a bird.

FIREBIRD Do not wish for enchantment. My curse is to fly always.

HOASANG You are enchanted?

FIREBIRD Yes, for all my life.

HOASANG Why?

FIREBIRD I cannot tell you or else you too will be enchanted.

HOASANG Never have I known such beauty. Being a Prince means nothing. My brothers would be happier without me.

FIREBIRD You would break your mother's heart.

HOASANG But she has two other sons.

FIREBIRD They are not great as you shall one day be. I must not take you away.

HOASANG (ACCEPTING FATE) And you cannot stay. Will I ever see you again?

FIREBIRD Only in your mind's eye.

HOASANG But I don't want dreams. Love must be seen, and heard, and touched.

FIREBIRD That is true. All I can give you is the key to love - with it you must open all the doors. Remember me always. Take this feather and keep it. It will bring you the world of love.

> HOASANG REMOVES HIS OUTER ROBE AND WE SEE HIM IN GOLD LIKE THE FIREBIRD. HE TAKES THE FEATHER. DAWN HAS BROKEN. SHE HAS GONE. HOASANG LOOKS AFTER HER, FOR- LORNLY HOLDING THE FEATHER. MUSIC ENDS.

> EMPRESS ENTERS TO HER OWN MUSIC ALMOST IMPATIENTLY. SHE IS FOLLOWED BY THE TWO PRINCES.

STAGE MANAGER
How many pieces in a broken heart?
Can it be mended
Or will it fall apart?
What of the Kingdom?
Who will win?
Oh Buddha
Let the answer begin.

EMPRESS Well, Hoasang, where is the bird?

HOASANG (LOST) The beautiful Firebird.

EMPRESS Yes, yes, where is she?

HOASANG Gone - she is gone.

EMPRESS But I told you to capture her.

HOASANG Capture?

EMPRESS Hoasang, where are you?

HOASANG I have flown south.

EMPRESS (SHAKING HIM) Stop this at once and tell me what happened last night.

MOATANG And no make-believe stories of Firebirds. We want proof!

EMPRESS Silence, Moatang! Come now, Hoasang, tell me what has befallen.

HOASANG My heart is broken, Mother.

EMPRESS (NOT BELIEVING AT FIRST) Because of the bird?

HOASANG Yes.

MOATANG Where is the proof that she ever came here?

HOASANG Here – this feather – it is hers. (MOATANG GRABS AT IT) No, don't touch it. She gave it to me.

SUNANG You love this spirit?

HOASANG Yes.

SUNANG But how can you love a bird?

HOASANG As one loves Buddha. My bird was an enchanted bird. She was once a Princess, and I have lost her.

EMPRESS It was my fault, my son. I was greedy and demanded you capture her. But sometimes we can hurt the things we love most.

HOASANG I would never have hurt her.

EMPRESS Then why didn't you capture her?

HOASANG Because she would die. She must fly always.

    SUNANG ACCIDENTALLY TOUCHES THE FEATHER AND THERE IS AN APPARENT CHANGE IN HIM.

SUNANG (STROKING HOASANG) My dear brother, we have always seen you laughing. I will give you my kingdom, if you will only smile.

    MOATANG GRABS AT THE FEATHER BUT THIS TIME TOUCHES IT. A CHANGE COMES OVER HIM.

MOATANG I too, Hoasang, will give up whatever belongs to me if only you will smile again.

HOASANG (AT LAST SEEING THE MIRACLE OF LOVE) Mother, brothers, you are all good and kind. May we always have such harmony and love. (SMILES AND KISSES THE FEATHER) You were right. It brought me the world of love. I shall give it to Buddha.

EMPRESS (STANDING ON HER DAIS) Good, my sons. You have all shown love. Now shall we fairly divide the Empire into three parts, each one of you to rule your part alone. Yet it shall be one great kingdom. Let its head be three kings, Sunang, Moatang and Hoasang.

    MUSIC.

STAGE MANAGER
The dance of the fans. (CLAPS)

ALL THREE SONS BOW TO THEIR MOTHER AND TO EACH OTHER. THEY THEN DO A DANCE OF THE FANS IN HONOUR OF THEIR MOTHER WHO FINALLY JOINS IN AND USES THE LARGEST FAN OF ALL. IT IS A DANCE OF UNITY.

THE COOK ENTERS BRIMMING WITH JOY, THROWING UP PAPER CHERRY BLOSSOMS IN THE AIR.

COOK Good news! Good news! Listen to me – I say good news. The cherries are growing all over the kingdom again. The trees are bursting with blossoms. The evil spirit has been captured. (TO THE STAGE MANAGER) Well, what do you say?

STAGE MANAGER (ADDRESSING THE AUDIENCE)
Honourable children
On this honourable day
We now end
This honourable play.

MUSIC AND DANCE FINALE. AT THE END THE STAGE MANAGER CLOSES THE SCREENS AND BOWS BEFORE EXITING.

END OF PLAY.

COSTUMES

MOATING   HOASANG   SUNANG

COOK   STAGE MANAGER

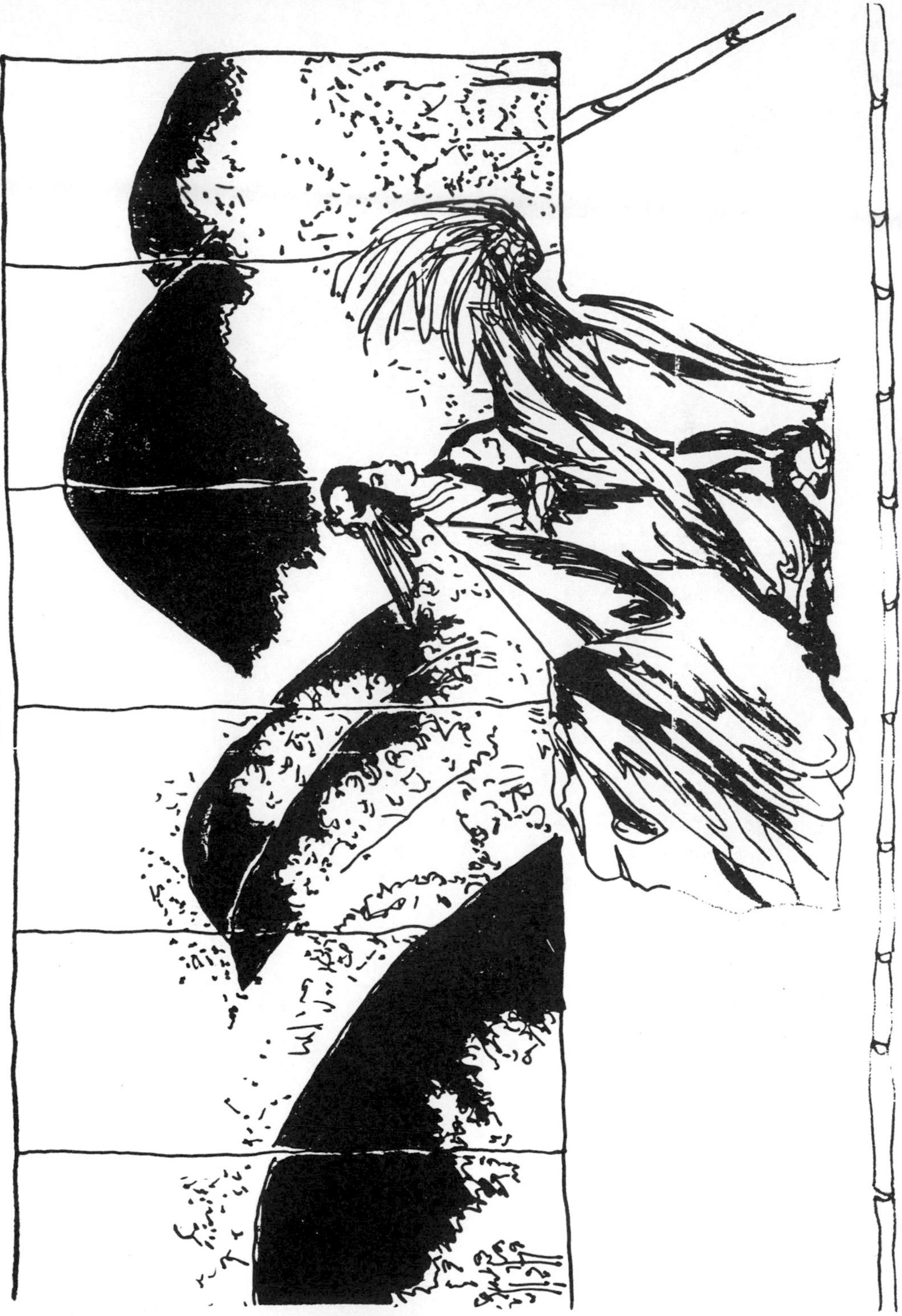

the Pied Piper

BY BLANCHE MARVIN

the Pied Piper
BY BLANCHE MARVIN

e magazine 20 west 43 street   new york 36, n. y.   longacre 3-7170

EMORY LEWIS, EDITOR

September 11, 1962

Theatre Critic

Blanche, my love--

I have been in the country for a month
and a half. I'm deep in a book of essays on
New York-- a record of my love affair with
Manhattan Island. I finished eight chapters
on vacation, so I'm desperately writing now,
seven days and seven nights a week, trying,
trying, trying to finish it.

Thus I did not see your play till now.
It is a lovely script, and I will make every
effort to see it. It's not that I don't want
to see Blanche Marvin productions, it's rather
that I cannot be more than one person at once.
But I do hope to see it this season, perhaps
with my daughter, Elodie, who is now two and
a half. Bravo for "Pied Piper."

Sincerely,
Emory Lewis

American Broadcasting Company

OUR MAN OFF BROADWAY TOOK HIS CHILDREN DOWN
TO THE CRICKET THEATRE LAST SATURDAY TO SEE
THE PIED PIPER......AND THE WHOLE FAMILY
RECOMMENDS THIS CHILDREN'S STORY DONE IN
SHAKESPEAREAN CLASSICAL STYLE. IT'S DONE
CHARMINGLY, IN HIGH STYLE BY AN ACCOMPLISHED
YOUNG CAST....THEY DON'T PLAY DOWN TO THE
CHILDREN--IN FACT THOSE UNDER FIVE PROBABLY
WON'T UNDERSTAND IT...BUT THE PIED PIPER WILL
PLEASE THE OLDER YOUNG SET AND ANY PARENTS
THEY MANAGE TO DRAG ALONG...FOR THE SATURDAY
PERFORMANCES.

David Shefrin
Director of News
WABC-TV

LEON PEARSON Feb 1,1963.
    5-6:30 TV Local Special NBC-TV
Something rather special is at the
Cricket Theatre on Second Ave. Fashio
especially for children, it's called,
"The Pied Piper" with Igor Youskevitc
as choreographer. It gives youngsters
the feeling of a Shakespearean production. Matinees tomorrow (Sat.)
at 1, 2:30, &4 PM.

Fun for the Young

11 Hollywood Dr
Plainview n.y.
Please Put me on your mailing
list. We saw "Pied Piper" last Sat
and loved it (my 5 yr old, about whom
we hesitated taking, was enthralled!)
Thank you and keep up the good work
Very truly yours
Mrs Eli Kaplan

THE PIED PIPER

King Aegis

Queen

Elizabeth

Town Crier/ Common man

Pied Piper / Player 1

Player 2

Place: Palace Courtyard extended to two wings of the Palace.
The town of Hamelin is beyond the walls.

Time: Elizabethan period.

The Pied Piper is to be produced in the Elizabethan Style and
Period in its movement, music and staging with set and costumes included. Like the Elizabethan playwrights who took
familiar stories and plays from the classics or history then
moulded them into the language, comedy and situations of their
own time, though the locations were not always English, I have
done the same. All that was necessary to add were some of the
Elizabethan play characteristics such as soliloquies, comics,
song and dance, disguised hero, tragedy involving deep emot-
ions, and multi scenes within the acts. Despite the advanced
language and more subdued movements, young children were held
by the vitality of the actors with the interspersed humour. It
is therefore essential that the acting is strong and skilled.

The well-known folk tale of the Pied Piper begins with a
stranger coming to the town of Hamelin - a town tormented and
overridden with rats. The stranger promises the mayor to rid
the town of the rats upon receipt of payment, a verbal agreement. The stranger pipes his tune and all the rats follow him
to the sea where they are drowned. But the mayor refuses to
abide by his agreement and the Pied Piper pipes his tune for
all the children who follow him to the mountains where they
disappear never to be seen again. The town is bereft of all its
children except for the one crippled boy left behind. It is the
Pied Piper who metes out justice.

In the Greek classic of the Orestes Trilogy, Orestes, disguised as a stranger, returns home to avenge his father's
murder by killing his Mother and Stepfather (not unlike Hamlet).
However, such an act was so unforgivable that only the Furies
(Conveyors of Justice) could save Orestes from death. It must
be noted that the Furies came disguised as Rats or Snakes and
appeared only when an unjust or punishable act was committed.
The Pied Piper adapted quite precisely into Elizabethan play
forms.

Pictures and programmes are indexed in the back of the book.

ACT ONE

THE STAGE IS DARK WITH ONLY A SPOT ON THE CHARACTER NOW ON STAGE. HE IS THE TOWNSMAN WHO HAS ENTERED CARRYING A BASKET FILLED WITH HATS AND PROPS. BY CHANGING HIS HAT HE BECOMES THE MERCHANT, THE BAKER, THE COBBLER, THE TAILOR. HE IS IN FACT ALL THE TOWNS-MEN. A LIKEABLE FELLOW THAT EVERYONE ENJOYS AND THE CHILDREN LOVE. HE CAN BE GOOD OR BAD, HAPPY OR SAD, CONNIVING OR HONEST. HE IS THE SALT OF THE EARTH -- THE SUGAR IN TOFFEE -- HE IS YOU -- HE IS ME -- HE IS EVERYONE -- YET NO ONE FOR HE IS THE COMMON MAN -- THE TOWNSMAN -- THE CITIZEN.

HE HAS BEEN WALKING A LONG TIME AND IS WEARY. HE PUTS DOWN HIS BASKET VERY CAREFULLY. HE IS WEARING A HAT OF THE TOWN CRIER. MUSIC COMPLEMENTS HIS SPEECH.

CRIER   I am carrying the world on my shoulders. It is good to put this load down. You see before you a basket -- no not just a basket, but the world. I am a Townsman of Hamelin -- I am a citizen of Hamelin -- nay I am all the citizens of Hamelin.

(ROAR OF THUNDER AND FLASHES OF LIGHTNING)

The skies have opened up and its torrents of tears will soon burst upon us. For what is rain but the tears of heaven. How can I shelter you -- my lovely basket -- my lovely world --

(HE RUNS TO HIDE IT TO NO AVAIL)

What would I be without you? (TO AUDIENCE) What would I be indeed? Ah the clouds have passed over. Right now -- as of this very moment -- I am the Town Crier of Hamelin. Two o'clock and all is well. Two o'clock and all is well.

(HE RINGS HIS BELL TWICE)

That task now done I will not be the Town Crier until 3! Then for one hour -- let me see -- just who is it that I shall be?

(TAKES OFF HIS HAT AND PUTS IT INTO THE BASKET, PICK-ING OUT DIFFERENT HATS, TRYING THEM ON -- CALLING OUT THE DIFFERENT CHARACTERS)

The Merchant, the Baker, the Cobbler, the Toymaker, the Butcher, the Miller, the Tailor, the Tiller.

(THE MUSIC CHANGES WITH EACH HAT AS DOES HIS CHAR-ACTER. HE MIME-DANCES EACH ONE'S WORK AND ENDS UP WITH THE TOWN CRIER'S HAT. HE THEN ARRANGES HIS HATS AS HE STARTS TO TALK IN SADDENED TONES, THE MUSIC NOW ENDED)

Alas it is 2 o'clock but all is not well. No indeed -- all is far from well. And what can we do?

(HE IS STILL BENDING OVER HIS BASKET AS TWO STROLLING PLAYERS COME STEALING IN. HE DOES NOT SEE THEM, BUT THEY SEE HIM.

TIP-TOEING OVER TO THE BASKET, THEY TIP THE TOWN CRIER INTO IT. EVERYTHING TOPPLES OVER, FALLING ALL OVER THE FLOOR. THE TOWN CRIER SCREAMS OUT)

Help! I am being robbed! Thieves!

THE STROLLING PLAYERS PUT THEIR HANDS OVER HIS MOUTH AND LOOK ROUND TO MAKE SURE NO ONE HAS SEEN, OR HEARD THE NOISE. THEY ARE DRESSED AS ELIZABETHAN STROLLING PLAYERS IN COLOURFUL COSTUMES AND UPON THEIR ENTRANCE WE BEGIN TO SEE A LITTLE BIT OF THE SET. THE TWO PLAYERS MUST BE VERY STYLISED IN THEIR MOVEMENT AND IN THE PATTER AND RHYME OF THEIR SPEECH -- ALMOST CLIPPED -- WITH MOVEMENTS TO MATCH. SHARP, CLEAR, ABRUPT.

THE SET IS REPRESENTATIONAL RATHER THAN REALISTIC. THE BACKDROP IS THE PAINTED TOWN OF HAMELIN WITH THE SEA IN THE BACKGROUND. TREES ARE ALL ABOUT -- AND IN THE FOREGROUND ARE THE WALL AND TOWER OF THE CASTLE. THE MAIN PART OF THE SET CONSISTS OF TWO LARGE ELIZ-ABETHAN STAGES REPRESENTING THE TWO HOUSES -- ONE OF THE PRESENT KING AND THE OTHER OF THE FORMER ROYAL HOUSE. EACH HAS ITS OWN COAT OF ARMS. THEY CAN BE PART OF THE PALACE -- ARRANGED SO THAT THE OPEN SPACE ON STAGE BECOMES THE PALACE COURTYARD. THERE IS ONE ADDITIONAL CENTRE PIECE WHICH BECOMES ALTAR AND SEAT OF JUSTICE, WHATEVER IS NECESSARY. TWO BENCHES ARE ALSO ON STAGE WHEREVER CONVENIENT AS PART OF THE COURTYARD.

PLAYER 1   Quiet fool -- we are not thieves. We will not harm you.

PLAYER 2   Do you call Strolling Players -- thieves?

HE PREENS HIMSELF LIKE A PEACOCK. THE TOWN CRIER TRIES TO ANSWER DESPITE THE HAND OVER HIS MOUTH. HIS HEAD AND EYES CONSTANTLY MOVE.

PLAYER 1   If I let you go -- will you keep quiet?

TOWN CRIER NODS "Y-E-S". THEY REMOVE THEIR HANDS. THE TOWN CRIER STARTS PICKING UP HIS HATS AND PROPS.

CRIER   Why are you here -- this time of night?

PLAYER 2   Does it matter where we are -- at any time of day or night?

CRIER   Well let me see -- er -- yes, I think you should be home and sleeping else something be wrong.

MUSIC.   PLAYER 1 SPEAKS TO PLAYER 2 WHO IS NOW MIM-ICKING THE TOWN CRIER.

PLAYER 1   Oho, something must be wrong if you are not home and asleep. But where is home? What is home? Naughty! Naughty!

THE SPEECH AND MOVEMENT ARE ALWAYS ALERT. IT IS AN ACT BETWEEN THE TWO PLAYERS AND THEY CONSTANTLY GO INTO IT. IT SHALL BE INDICATED FROM HERE ON AS "ACTING".

PLAYER 2   (ACTING) Wrong indeed. I have no home. That's very wrong!

(WEEPS FAKE TEARS BRUSHING THEM FROM HIS EYES WITH HUGE MOVEMENT)

How can I sleep when there is no place to put my head down?

(HAND ON HEAD AS IN COMMEDIA DELL' ARTE)

PLAYER 1   (ACTING) There! There -- my tender one -- Home is where the head is. The ground is soft -- soft as a bed -- lay thee down.

(GIVES PLAYER 2 A HARD SHOVE WHO THEN PRAT FALLS ON THE GROUND. HE IMMEDIATELY FALLS ASLEEP WITH GREAT PRETENCE -- EVEN SNORING)

No sooner said than done. What next, kind friend?

END OF MUSIC.

CRIER   (STILL PICKING UP HATS) You are very amusing fellows -- but you will not laugh for long. Know you what town this is?

PLAYER 2   (ABRUPTLY UP FROM SLEEP) Hamelin -- is it not?

CRIER   It is indeed! And know you the curse of Hamelin?

PLAYERS 1 & 2 (HUGGING EACH OTHER IN PRETENDED FEAR) No?

CRIER   Ha -- we have been cursed -- these past few months -- with R-A-T-S.

PLAYERS 1 & 2 (TO MUSIC) With Rats!!!

THE TWO PLAYERS GET DOWN ON ALL FOURS AND START CHASING EACH OTHER -- THEY CRAWL TO THE TOWN CRIER AND BITE HIM -- HE JUMPS SKY HIGH. MUSIC ENDS.

CRIER   Stop this mockery. This pretending! The Rats have over-run Hamelin. Neither poison -- nor traps will kill them.

THE TWO PLAYERS GO ON WITH THEIR PLAY AS THE TOWN CRIER TALKS. THEY HAVE TAKEN FROM HIS BASKET A BOLT OF CLOTH WHICH THEY HAVE UNROLLED WITH THEIR MOUTHS WHILE STILL ON ALL FOURS. THE CLOTH IS FILLED WITH HOLES THROUGH WHICH THEY PLAY PEEK-A-BOO. THEY EN-TANGLE THE TOWN CRIER IN THE CLOTH -- HIS FOOT GETS CAUGHT IN ONE OF THE HOLES.

CRIER   Play if you will but that will be the last of our beautifully woven cloth. Hamelin, famous for its cloth -- and look at what is left.

> (THEY NOW PLAY SKIP ROPE WITH THE CLOTH ENDING UP BY WINDING IT ROUND THE TOWN CRIER LIKE A MUMMY. ON HIS LAST WORDS OF THE FOLLOWING SPEECH THEY WIND THE LAST PIECE ROUND HIS MOUTH)

Unwind the cloth. We are to be pitied in Hamelin.

> (THEY PULL OFF THE CLOTH AND TWIRL TOWN CRIER AROUND WITH LIGHTENING SPEED)

This is no joking matter. We are poor -- starved.

> (A COMPLETE TRANSITION HERE FOR ALL. IT IS SERIOUS AND GENUINELY SAD AS THE PLAYERS HELP ENACT THE STORY)

The Rats have stolen the food from our very mouths. Why, only yesterday I was baking bread -- pardon me -- my hat --

> (HE GETS BAKER'S HAT AND PUTS IT ON. MUSIC STARTS)

-- when a storm of Rats descended -- and ate all of the bread that I had just finished baking.

> (THE PLAYERS HAVE BECOME THE RATS -- STEALING LOAVES OF BREAD FROM THE BASKET AND FINALLY TAKING THE ONE LOAF HELD BY THE TOWN CRIER. THIS IS ALL A DANCE)

When little Edward came in to buy bread for his Mother --

> (PLAYER 1 BECOMES EDWARD -- CHANGING CLOTHES ONLY SLIGHTLY BUT USING A STICK AS A CRUTCH)

-- there was none left. All that way on a crutch and then no bread. (SADLY) Not even for the good little Edward... not even for him would (SPOKEN QUIETLY; LOOKING ROUND BEFORE SAYING THE WORD) the F-U-R-I-E-S -- save their wrath.

> MUSIC ENDS. THE TWO PLAYERS BECOME AFRAID IN EARNEST.

PLAYER 1   Furies -- the Furies are in Hamelin?

CRIER   And what else are these RATS that overrun our city?

PLAYER 2   'Tis true the Furies come disguised in many shapes and forms -- but would they take the very bread away from a crippled child?

PLAYER 1   They would have to be very angry indeed. What has happened in Hamelin?

CRIER   We are not sure -- but ten years ago -- our good King Amnon died -- his son Orin was the rightful heir but too young to rule --

PLAYER 2   Wait! We heard tell of this story. It is a play we ourselves enact -- Listen and see if it is not the same story.

MUSIC. PLAYER 2 PUTS ON THE CROWN AND DRAPES A CLOAK OVER HIS SHOULDERS, TAKING HIS COSTUME OUT OF HIS BAG. PLAYER 1, BEING QUITE SHORT, PUTS ON A WIG TO GIVE HIM A FULL HEAD OF HAIR. HE BECOMES A YOUNG BOY OF 11 BY HIS STANCE. PLAYER 2 SITS ON THE BENCH WHICH HAS BEEN ON STAGE LEFT. PLAYER 1 GOES UP TO KING, BOWS AND SPEAKS.

PLAYER 1   (WEEPING) Oh my uncle -- my father is dead.

PLAYER 2   (EVIL) Ah -- my little **one** -- you must not weep -- for you must now act as a man.

PLAYER 1   But I weep for my father. (FRIGHTENED) I am now King.

PLAYER 2   There are grave decisions to make here and now. You are not ready to be King. You must be taught first. I shall wear the crown till you are ready.

PLAYER 1 LOOKS UP TO SEE THE CROWN ON THE HEAD OF THE KING FOR THE FIRST TIME.

PLAYER 1   I have lost both Father and Crown. Uncle, what would you have me do?

PLAYER 2   You have not lost the crown. You must only prepare for it. A boat awaits you in the harbour. It will take you to a land far away where you will be taught well. A change of home will stop you grieving and you will learn to become King. Go now.

PLAYER 1   (URGENTLY) But Uncle -- I wish to stay. My mother and sister have need of me.

PLAYER 2   Hamelin has greater need. You must serve it first. Go quickly.

PLAYER 1   (PLEADINGLY) May I not bid farewell to my mother and sister?

PLAYER 2   No -- it will only sadden you all the more.

PLAYER 1   One little good-bye to them.

PLAYER 2   There are no good-byes. You shall return when you are ready.

PLAYER 1   And when will that be?

PLAYER 2   When you are of age.

PLAYER 1   Uncle -- when will I be of age?

PLAYER 2   (ANGRY) When? When? When? When the time comes! Go now.

PLAYER 1   Farewell, Uncle. Farewell, Hamelin.

PLAYER 2   (VERY MELODRAMATICALLY) At last I am King! And so shall I remain, even when the boy comes of age. He does not know it but he is banished from Hamelin, forever. And when he is 21, I shall announce his death. I have many many years to com-fort his mother, the Queen. Ten whole years to reign freely -- and those ten shall multiply themselves till they shall be my whole lifetime. For I shall remain King until my death.

  HE STROLLS OFF. THE MUSIC ENDS.

CRIER   Come back! Both of you come back. And tell me how you know this story. For it is our story -- the very same -- come back, I say.

  (PLAYERS 1 AND 2 RETURN DRESSED AS AT PLAY'S START)

You called Hamelin by name.

PLAYER 1   It is our tragic piece. We always name the town we play.

CRIER   It is tragic, indeed. But how do you know this story? Ten years have now passed. (LOOKS VERY CLOSELY AT THE PLAY-ERS) Is one of you Orin? Returning for the crown? Answer me, I pray.

PLAYER 2   We are strolling players -- ACTORS. We can play the part of KINGS -- VILLAINS -- HEROES -- but we are none of them.

CRIER   (VERY DELIBERATELY) Maybe you should know that our King Aegis marries Orin's mother -- (TO PLAYER 2) -- our former Queen -- (TO PLAYER 1) -- tomorrow, or rather today.

  HE LOOKS FOR THEIR REACTION. THEY ARE STARTLED BY
  THE NEWS BUT TRY TO HIDE IT.

PLAYER 1   (REFUSING TO COMMIT HIMSELF) More to add to our tragic play. The King ten years later -- marries the former Queen.

CRIER   You understand that the town of Hamelin wishes for this royal wedding to take place. We pray for it to happen.

PLAYER 2   Why so?

CRIER   Why then the Plague of Rats will disappear. The Furies will have been avenged. Justice will have triumphed. Hamelin will be free.

  HE SEARCHES FOR A HAT WITH EACH SENTENCE, SO THAT
  EACH OF THE TOWNSFOLK IS REPRESENTED.

PLAYER 1   And the evil King will remain.

PLAYER 2   What justice is that!

CRIER   Ah -- but then you do not understand.

PLAYER 1   No -- we do not understand.
    (STARTS TO PLAY-ACT MOCKINGLY THROUGH THE FOLLOWING
    SCENE: SLAPPING PLAYER 2)
King -- evil King.
    (MUSIC CUE)
Know then that I am a Fury -- gr, grrr -- disguised as a -- a
-- RAT! However, I shall disappear from the face of this town
if -- if -- if -- if --

PLAYER 2   If what? Pray tell me, Fury.

PLAYER 1   If you marry the old, oh pardon -- the former Queen.

PLAYER 2   Marry? The former Queen of the dead King Amnon?
And then you will leave Hamelin? But, why marry?

PLAYER 1   If you marry the former Queen why then she will be
a Queen once more and her daughter a Princess.

PLAYER 2   I must say that though I am King, the Queen is a bit
confusing. However if I marry the former Queen, she will just
become another Queen -- my Queen. And what say you of that
boy I banished? Will you be content to leave him far away in a
strange land?

PLAYER 1   Aha, well let me see. Why was it I came here in the
first place? I cannot remember.

    HE MIMES TRYING TO THINK. END OF MUSIC.

CRIER   Stop your constant mockery. The former Queen marries
King Aegis today and Hamelin will rejoice at having her Queen
once more.

PLAYER 1   (POUNCING ON TOWN CRIER) But what of the banished
Orin?

PLAYER 2   Suppose one of us -- is he!

PLAYER 1   Where is your justice?

PLAYER 2   Have not ten years passed? Time for the crown to be
given to Orin?

PLAYER 1   The crown is rightfully Orin's.

CRIER   (TERRIFIED) But he hasn't returned. Therefore the King
is still King.

PLAYER 2   What fools live in this town of Hamelin. The King is King rightly or wrongly. Evil as he may be, he remains King.

PLAYER 1   Let us flee from Hamelin. They shall have no Strolling Players -- no laughter.

CRIER   (RELIEVED) You will not stay for the wedding?

PLAYER 2   Shall we perform for the King? What say you, my friend?

PLAYER 1   I say we go -- to greener fields.
>   MUSIC CUE.

PLAYER 2   Shall we disappear -- like this scarf?
>   (HE DOES A MAGICAL TRICK)

Would you prefer green for the bride?
>   (SCARF COMES BACK GREEN AS HE CHANGES ITS COLOURS)

Or red?
>   END MUSIC CUE.

CRIER   I am only a townsman -- and you are an actor, a magician. But I am the merchant, the baker, the cobbler, the toymaker, the butcher, the miller, the tailor, the tiller.
>   (TO MUSIC HE PUTS ON HIS MANY HATS AND DANCES AS
>   PLAYER 2 TAKES OUT HIS FIFE AND PIPES A TUNE. PLAYER
>   1 IS BUSY JUGGLING AS THEY FOLLOW PLAYER 2 - THEY
>   ALMOST LEAVE WHEN THE TOWN CRIER CALLS OUT)

Stop the music a moment. (PLAYER 2 STOPS) Whatever will happen from now on -- will happen. Whoever you are. (TO THE PLAYERS) I cannot turn back or forth the pages of time. They will follow as the Fates decree. A man's hand is only the hand of a man. Whether he changes the colours of a scarf from green to red by magic -- he is only a man. But Fate's hand cannot be changed. As you will see.

PLAYER 2   Shall I play my tune?

CRIER   No, wait but a moment --
>   (HE LOOKS AT THE TIME AND IS SHOCKED. MUSIC CUE)

It is almost 5 -- I must be gone. When did the hours of 3 and 4 arrive? They fled my sight. But who will know. I'll journey back with dawn aglow.
>   (PLAYER 2 PLAYS HIS TUNE. THE DANCE RESUMES, THE TOWN
>   CRIER WITH THE HATS. PLAYER 1 JUGGLES. THEY GAILY EXIT
>   WITH DAWN ABOUT TO BREAK AND TOWN CRIER CALLING OUT:)

5 o'clock and all is well. 5 o'clock and all is well!

CURTAIN.

END OF ACT ONE.

ACT TWO

> STILL BEFORE DAWN. WE NOW SEE MORE OF THE SET. FROM
> THE ELIZABETHAN STAGE, TO BE REFERRED TO AS HOUSE,
> ON STAGE LEFT, COMES ELIZABETH, A YOUNG BROODING
> GIRL OF 16. HER UNCLE IS KING -- HIS HOUSE IS STAGE
> RIGHT. SHE IS PACING BACK AND FORTH FILLED WITH GRIEF,
> FEAR AND DOUBT. HER SCENE IS ONE OF RELENTLESS TOR-
> MENT. MUSIC.

ELIZABETH Oh friendly night -- whose fateful hours have
cast the sleep of innocence on Hamelin's head, bring me peace.
I cannot sleep. I am driven by despair. (WEEPS) Alas -- my
mother marries the evil King. Oh, Orin, ten years have passed.
I pray you return now for your crown. Even the Furies cry for
your Justice. Tonight I will not sleep for there is a current in
the air almost like music --

> (WE HEAR PLAYER 2'S MUSIC HERE)

-- as Fate decides what will happen. (SHE SHIVERS) And yet my
own grief must be put aside -- for tomorrow -- no today -- my
mother once Queen shall be a bride. Oh weep for her weakness.
My father dead -- my brother banished -- my mother's home
deserted. Oh house -- oh King -- oh pity. A ghost for a
husband. A tomb for a home. Tormentuous tears. Oh fleeting
night -- fly quickly -- and with it come the deciding dawn.
Prove all my fears to be false.

> (IN TERROR AS IF SHE SEES THE KING)

What if the King should not listen to a woman's tears? What
then would my mother do? And what of Orin -- does he live?
Dark dreams on slipping fingers from grief sometimes springs
hate -- then revenge. (PLEADING) God! Unmeasured evil can be
crushed? Your lightening can strike down mountains. Come dawn
-- come peace -- come my mother's Wedding Day!

> SHE SITS WEEPING AS DAWN GENTLY BREAKS. STAGE LIGHTS
> GRADUALLY BRING US A BEAUTIFUL DAWN AND FOR THE
> FIRST TIME WE SEE THE SET FULLY. ELIZABETH FALLS
> ASLEEP WITH THE DAWN.

> THE QUEEN ENTERS FROM HOUSE STAGE LEFT. A STATELY
> WOMAN WITH COOL AND REGAL BEARING. HER FEARS ARE
> CONTROLLED THOUGH QUITE EVIDENTLY SHE IS A WEAK
> WOMAN WHO TRIES TO APPEASE EVERYONE. HER TURMOIL
> HASN'T THE STRENGTH OF ELIZABETH. HER CONTROL IS A
> COMPLETE CONTRAST TO ELIZABETH'S IMPASSIONED GRIEF.
> SHE DOES NOT SEE ELIZABETH AT FIRST.

QUEEN (THINKING HERSELF ALONE) The coolness of early morning comforts me. Today my feelings are double-edged. My pledge
of marriage should be of love past limit -- yet it is my doom
past cure. Love should seal the heart of bride and groom. Yet
my seal of marriage is my seal of doom. (SHE TREMBLES) No --
no -- it will not be so. God prove me right -- that good con-

quers wrong. For if I prove wrong, what then is right?

(SEES ELIZABETH ASLEEP AND AWAKENS HER GENTLY)

Elizabeth - my daughter have you slept here all night? Come child, let me warm you.

ELIZABETH (WAKING SLOWLY) Warm me Mother? Can you warm the icy oceans -- the cyclones that whirl inside me? But I must not forget today and wear a happy face.

QUEEN My Wedding Day is for you, for Orin, if he lives, and all of Hamlin. Should I refuse the marriage and have us all face danger?

ELIZABETH Yes! It is always better to face the truth and fight for it.

QUEEN (URGENTLY) I know the King only marries me to keep the crown and to silence the Furies.

ELIZABETH And knowing this -- you still marry him? Oh, Mother, you only bring the danger closer!

QUEEN I avoid the danger. The King would kill for the crown -- but would not kill my children if I am his Queen.

ELIZABETH You speak of him with mercy. But he has none. Do not marry him for my sake or for Orin's.

SPECIAL LIGHTING EFFECT.

QUEEN Let us not judge but let the Furies decide. If the Plague of Rats disappear when I become his bride then the wedding and the crown are just. And by that judgement you must abide.

ELIZABETH Mother, you ask too much of me. The King's not taken the crown justly. When Father lived -- there was a King. I beg you wed not such an evil thing.

END OF SPECIAL LIGHTING EFFECT.

QUEEN What else can I do, but pray this marriage will change all of that. Where else could we go?

ELIZABETH Go? The house of Arter -- the Royal House -- leave Hamelin? No, my Mother we must fight. We must stay and wait for Orin's return.

QUEEN (DESPERATELY) And what if he does not return? What if he is dead? What then?

ELIZABETH (STRONGLY CONVINCED) News of his death would carry quickly. Our King would be the first to know.

QUEEN If he lives and still does not return, what then?

ELIZABETH   He will. Else all my living is in vain. He will return! Then what will you do?

QUEEN   (GIVING UP) We must prepare for the wedding. I beg you, Elizabeth be gracious to the King and do not speak of your brother's return.

ELIZABETH (BITTERLY) Already I am forced into silence.

QUEEN   (APPEASINGLY) But not forever. First let us make the King content -- then we will look for our lost Orin.

ELIZABETH   (WITH DISGUST) We are a mockery.

QUEEN   We are compromising. It is better to give in a little than to lose all.

ELIZABETH   To give in to evil, even a little, is to lose all.

> KING SUDDENLY APPEARS FROM HIS HOUSE. A STRONG HANDSOME MAN WHOSE EVIL IS APPARENT. HE SPEAKS SHARPLY. HIS WALK IS A CEREMONIAL MOVEMENT TO MUSIC. HE SEES BOTH WOMEN BUT IGNORES ELIZABETH. WHEN HE DOES SPEAK TO ELIZABETH, HE IS SARCASTIC AND CONDESCENDING. THE TENSION IS TREMENDOUS UPON SEEING HIM.

KING   Up so early? Are you fretting over the wedding? Or plotting?

QUEEN   Oh, my King! A woman on her Wedding Day cannot sleep.

KING   (CRUELLY) I slept well except for one devilish dream I had about Elizabeth.

> QUEEN GOES QUICKLY TO KING TO DISTRACT HIM FROM ELIZABETH. AS THE KING PACES BACK AND FORTH ANXIOUSLY, THE QUEEN FOLLOWS HIM, FRIGHTENED BY HIS MOOD.

QUEEN   Come -- let me comfort you.

> ELIZABETH SITS STARING AT HIM WITH DISDAIN. THE KING LOOKS BACK AT HER AND THEN PUSHES ASIDE THE QUEEN. HE FEELS HE MUST SHOW ELIZABETH HIS POWER.

KING   And you, Elizabeth -- no words of comfort for the King?

ELIZABETH   My King -- I did not ask to be present in your dreams. As for comfort -- my mother has given you enough for all of us. (SHE STARTS TO LEAVE)

KING   (COMMANDING) Stay!

ELIZABETH   No, my King. Only by royal command would I stay. (SARCASTICALLY) But this is your Wedding Day.

KING IS FURIOUS BUT ELIZABETH LEAVES.

QUEEN   She meant no harm.

KING   She is relentless.

QUEEN   Relentless in her grief.

KING   She lives for only one thing.

QUEEN   And that is?

KING   Orin's return to Hamelin.

QUEEN   (FEARFUL) No, my Lord. She remains the little girl she used to be when her father and brother lived in the same house. But that is no more. Elizabeth still lingers in the past. She sees neither the present nor the future. Give her time.

KING   (FIERCELY) Time! Time has run out, my dear. The ten years have passed. Still I intend to remain King until my death. (HYPOCRITICALLY) But come -- today is a day of rejoicing -- of a beginning -- our happiness.

QUEEN   (TIMIDLY) I had hoped our happiness would bring happiness to all of Hamelin.

KING   And so it shall. Our marriage will quiet the Furies!

QUEEN   I pray it will.

KING   (IRRITATED) Of course, it will. The Palace has been free of Rats. The Furies approve of this marriage.

QUEEN   A good sign from the Heavens?

KING   (SHARPLY) It is! Our marriage will rid Hamelin of its Plague of Rats, making us prosperous once more and filling the coffers with golden coins.

HE SHAKES THE NEAR-EMPTY MONEY PURSE.

QUEEN   My King -- without displeasing -- I must ask --

KING   (IRRITATED) What is it, Lady?

QUEEN   What would you do -- to -- Orin should he return?

KING   Lady, he is dead. He died a long time ago --
   (QUEEN BEGINS TO FAINT. KING HOLDS HER FIRMLY)

on the boat when he left Hamelin. His death will be announced today and I shall remain King. Your hand, my Lady, on our Wedding Day.

QUEEN HOLDS OUT HER HAND IN TERROR. MUSIC BEGINS. THEY EXIT IN A PATTERNED MOVEMENT.

TOWN CRIER AND THE PLAYERS ENTER EXACTLY AS WE HAD SEEN THEM ON THEIR LAST EXIT. THE TOWN CRIER ENTERS FROM DOWN STAGE LEFT, HIS USUAL WAY, WHICH MUST BE ESTABLISHED THROUGHOUT THE PLAY. IT IS THE DIRECTION FROM THE TOWN. THE TWO PLAYERS ARE JUGGLING YET NEVER TAKE THEIR EYES OFF THE TOWN CRIER. THROUGHOUT THE SCENE THEY KEEP ON JUGGLING, NEVER SAYING A WORD. THE TOWN CRIER TRIES TO MAKE THEM SPEAK BUT DOES NOT SUCCEED.

CRIER   (TO PLAYERS)
As you can see
I need not tell
We are not well
We are not well
If you be Orin
Tell me pray
That we may know
On this Wedding Day.

        (TO THE CHILDREN)
These Strolling Players are discontent
Elizabeth will not relent
The proud King will not repent
Only the Queen makes a weak attempt.
Despite all this I prepare to be
Arranger of the Wedding Ceremony.

        HE PICKS A FLOWER OUT OF THE BASKET AND PUTS IT ON. THE PLAYERS SILENTLY PUT ON FLOWERS TOO. THE TOWN CRIER LOOKS AT THEM -- SHRUGS HIS SHOULDERS -- TAKES HIS BELL -- AND CALLS OUT.

CRIER
6 o'clock and all is well.
6 o'clock and all is well.

                    BLACKOUT.

SCENE TWO

        SAME SETTING AS ACT 1. THE CURTAINS OPEN ON THE TOWN CRIER ALONE WITH HIS BASKET. HE IS WEAVING A WREATH OF FLOWERS. THE BASKET NOW HAS HOLES IN IT FROM THE RATS. MUSIC.

CRIER   (SADLY) There's little time before the wedding and I must finish these wreaths of flowers. A wedding should mean joy. Perhaps there will be joy. Oh -- but I forgot -- my farmer's cap.

        (GOES TO THE BASKET LOOKING FOR A HAT. HE PULLS OUT ONE FILLED WITH HOLES)

They've even eaten you -- poor thing.

(HE PUTS THE HAT BACK, FINDS THE FARMER'S CAP. PUTS IT ON HIS HEAD. HIS WHOLE CHARACTER CHANGES WITH IT AS HE BECOMES THE FARMER)

(JOYFULLY) Now mind you -- I am a goodly farmer -- and today is the wedding of our King. Here are my wreaths, my flowers! Oh lovely sun whose light blesses the Earth -- creates the magic of life -- the colours we could not see but for your kindness -- what a glorious day you bestow upon us for the Royal wedding. A wedding -- the building of a new nest -- another Spring -- the hope of life.

HE IS HAPPY AS HE ARRANGES THE FLOWERS. HIS GRATITUDE TO THE SUN, AS IN ACT 1, HIS FEAR OF RAIN AS THE TOWN CRIER, IS ALL PART OF THE COMMON MAN'S LOVE, FEAR AND NEED OF THE NATURAL ELEMENTS. IT IS NOT THE POET BUT THE ORDINARY MAN WHO IS SO DEPENDENT ON NATURE. IN A MIME DANCE HE PLACES FLOWERS AROUND THE COURTYARD. THE MUSIC IS LIVELY. HE STOPS SUDDENLY WHEN SEEING ELIZABETH. SHE HAS BEEN WALKING A LONG TIME AND IS WEARY. A BLACK VEIL IS UPON HER HEAD -- HER SADDENED FACE MATCHES ITS SOMBRENESS. SHE HAS COME IN FROM STAGE LEFT WHERE THE STEPS FROM OUTSIDE THE THEATRE ALSO LEAD ONTO THE STAGE. THIS FEELING OF COMING FROM FAR AWAY IS IMPORTANT.

ELIZABETH   Good farmer -- I beg you - no more dancing. Spread your flowered wreaths if you must -- but do it in silence. I should take those wreaths -- your wreaths of joy -- and put them on my father's grave.

FARMER   For one so young, why do you speak of the grave? There should be laughter from your lips.

ELIZABETH   Then who would weep for my father? Who will bring back my brother? And you make wreaths for the wedding.

FARMER   Who knows? This wedding may free us all!

ELIZABETH   You are blind to the King's evil. But the children of the House of Arter, my father's house -- have a wrong to be made right.

FARMER   Let Fate decide for you.

ELIZABETH   Fool -- blind -- fool.

(HER PATIENCE IS EXHAUSTED. MUSIC. SPECIAL LIGHTING)

The Furies have begun the battle. The fight is almost through Hamelin is besieged by rats. What more proof need there be for you?

SPECIAL LIGHT ENDS. TOWN CRIER REMOVES HIS FARMER'S CAP. HE STANDS BEWILDERED. THEN PUTS ON HIS ORIGINAL

47

HAT. WE HEAR THE PIPING MUSIC AS THE TWO PLAYERS COME DOWN THE AISLE -- PLAYING ONLY TO THE CHILDREN -- STOPPING AND DANCING FOR THEM.

CRIER   (FRIGHTENED) They have returned. (FRANTIC) 10 o'clock and all is well. Let this be a happy day!! Let the wedding take place -- without trouble.

PLAYER 1   Town Crier -- are you dancing for the wedding?

PLAYER 2   (ACTING) Oh joyous day -- oh Wedding Day. Come, friend -- a posy.

(THEY ARE ON STAGE BY NOW. PLAYER 2 TAKES A FLOWERED WREATH AND PUTS IT ON PLAYER 1'S HEAD. IT FALLS OVER HIS EYES. HE PUSHES IT UP, BUT IT KEEPS FALLING ONTO HIS NOSE)

Aha -- a true nose-gay! My bride -- beloved.

(HE BENDS ON ONE KNEE TO PLAYER 1 WHO ACTS LIKE A BLUSHING BRIDE)

Take my hand in marriage or I'll take your head instead.

(HE SLITS THE THROAT OF PLAYER 1 BY HAND)

PLAYER 1   (FALSETTO VOICE) I'm yours -- only leave my head be. I am yours.

CRIER   It is almost time for the wedding -- I beg you -- leave.

DANCE MOVEMENT AND MUSIC.

PLAYER 1   We are not invited.

PLAYER 2   He would have us leave --

PLAYER 1   What say you?

PLAYER 2   I say we stay --

PLAYER 1   Let us stay and play.

PLAYER 2   Musicians for the Wedding Day --

THEY DANCE VIGOROUSLY WHILE THE TOWN CRIER IS AT A LOSS AS TO WHAT TO DO.

CRIER   (TO CHILDREN) At least they'll bring laughter to the wedding.

(THEIR MUSIC BECOMES GAYER. THE TOWN CRIER CANNOT CONTAIN HIMSELF AND SO JOINS THEM IN THEIR DANCE)

Why this music will not let me stop dancing!

(THE MUSIC AND DANCING BUILD TO HEIGHTS OF GAIETY FOR ALL THREE)

If only we could entice the Rats of Hamlin with such music.

(THE PIPING STOPS SUDDENLY AS PLAYER 2 LOOKS PIERC-
INGLY AT THE TOWN CRIER)

But why stop playing?

PLAYER 2   (NOT ANSWERING HIS QUESTION) You asked me who I
was -- now I will tell you. I am the Pied Piper.

CRIER   Yes -- indeed you are -- and the tunes you play charm
all of Hamelin. Play on!

PLAYER 2   Suppose I should rid Hamelin of its Rats -- by the
pipe I play!

CRIER   (DISBELIEVING) Yes -- well. Wait till after the wedding.

PLAYER 1   But suppose the Rats come to the wedding?

PLAYER 2   Are the Rats here at the Palace?

CRIER   No -- the Rats have not reached the Palace -- as yet.

PLAYER 1   (TO PLAYER 2) Then the King is not afraid.

PLAYER 2   (TO PLAYER 1) He knows nothing. All the better.

CRIER   Why the whisper? What plots are you plotting?

PLAYER 2   None. We will wait till after the wedding -- then ask
the King to rid Hamelin of its Rats.

CRIER   (RELIEVED) Oh, good gentlemen -- how kind -- how --

HE RUNS AND EMBRACES THEM.

PLAYER 2   (ACTING) Please -- I beg you -- I shall blush with
shame. (ENACTS A BASHFUL LADY)

CRIER   I was truly afraid you might anger the King before the
Wedding. Mum's the word?

PLAYER 2   Mum it shall be.

ELIZABETH HAS RETURNED FROM HER FATHER'S GRAVE. SHE
REMOVES HER VEIL AND SEES THE TWO PLAYERS.

ELIZABETH   (TO TOWN CRIER) Who are these men -- these
strangers on the Palace ground?

CRIER   Why -- they -- (STARTS FUMBLING FOR WORDS) -- they
are just that -- ah -- ah -- strangers to Hamelin.

ELIZABETH   And why have they come?

CRIER   To -- to -- to -- to -- to -- rid Hamelin of the Rats.

THE PLAYERS GLARE AT HIM.

ELIZABETH   Let me speak to them alone.

PLAYER 2   May I speak for both of us. My friend is mum -- ah -- mute.

TOWN CRIER & PLAYER 1 LOOK UP STARTLED. PLAYER 2 GIVES THEM A SIGN TO GO. BEWILDERED THEY EXIT WITH BASKET.

ELIZABETH   Stranger, where do you come from?

MUSIC OF PIPER BEGINS.

PLAYER 2   From a land beyond the sea.

ELIZABETH   And what land is that? (SUSPICION SLOWLY CHANGES) No -- say nothing. I know you and yet you are a stranger to me.

PLAYER 2   (AVOIDING HER EYES) Will you go to the wedding today?

ELIZABETH   (STILL LOST IN HER THOUGHTS ABOUT THE STRANGER) Wedding? Yes, the wedding.

PLAYER 2   (RESOLVED NOW TO GAIN HER FULL ATTENTION, TO CAPTURE HER THOUGHTS) You said you knew me. How so?

ELIZABETH   I don't know. Tell me your plan to rid Hamelin of its plague.

THIS FOR ELIZABETH IS ONLY A WAY OF TRYING TO IDENT-IFY THE MAN. SHE IS NOT SURE IF HE IS FRIEND OR FOE. THEREFORE SHE HAS BEEN ON GUARD ALL ALONG.

PLAYER 2   I have come to avenge the Furies.

(NO RECOGNITION FROM ELIZABETH -- IN DESPERATION)

Sister! -- you wept for me -- all these years and yet when you see me -- you do not know me.

ELIZABETH   (IN ALMOST WILD JOY) Orin! It is you! My brother Orin!! (SHE RUNS TO EMBRACE HIM. SHE LOOKS AT HIM AND STOPS)

(MUSIC HAS BEEN PLAYING THROUGHOUT. IT CHANGES HERE)

No -- not Orin. (TURNS FROM HIM) You are not Orin. I would know him instantly. Stranger -- you have come to claim the crown! Where is my brother?

ORIN   Oh sister mine. (HE GOES TO HER) Look here -- upon my brow -- the scar remains where I wounded myself with the first sword Father gave me. Remember how you wept and brought me your most treasured doll --

ELIZABETH   (COMPLETE RECOGNITION) Oh Orin -- Orin -- to have waited so long to see you and then not know you.

(THEY RUN TO EACH OTHER AND EMBRACE)

Forgive me -- forgive me. I have lived in fear too long. Oh, Orin.

ORIN   Oh, Elizabeth, you are the same little girl I always remembered. Time walked without you. You remain as you always were, my little sister. But the years have made a man of me.

ELIZABETH   Let me look at you -- my princely brother -- my rightful King. A Strolling Player? A vagabond?

THEY EMBRACE.

ORIN   I am home now.

ELIZABETH   Home?

ORIN   Home. Whatever changes there are, it is still home.

ELIZABETH   (AFRAID) Oh, Orin, I tremble now with new despair. You are not safe and no one will help you.

ORIN   (COMFORTINGLY) Sister dear, no one from the outside can mend the wound of our bleeding house. We must undo the evil deeds. And now, on my returning day, let us both pray.

THE TWO NOW KNEEL ON THE ALTER WHERE THE FLOWERED WREATHS LIE. THEY ASK BLESSINGS FROM THEIR FATHER. A NEW STRAIN OF MUSIC IS HEARD.

ELIZABETH   Dearest Father -- once King -- help deliver us.

ORIN   Let us defeat those who defeated us. Send forth Justice to defend our cause.

ELIZABETH   Hear our cry -- have pity and forgive. For through our blood alone will your House live.

MUSIC AND PRAYER END. ORIN DISCLOSES HIS PLAN. SPECIAL LIGHTING.

ORIN
Go, my sister -- prepare for the Wedding Day.
I -- with this pipe, the tunes will play.
And with it, all the Rats of Hamelin carry away.
But for this deed, the King must pay my due.
Or else all Hamelin will be through
Now go -- say nothing to anyone
Keep silent -- or I will be undone.

SHE KISSES HIS HAND, AND GOES TO HER HOUSE.

SPECIAL LIGHTING ENDS. FADE-OUT.

SCENE THREE

> THE TOWN CRIER ENTERS AS USUAL DOWN-STAGE LEFT. HE
> IS NOW THE TOWN ELDER WHO WILL PERFORM THE WEDDING
> CEREMONY. HIS BASKET IS CARRIED ALONG WITH HIM BUT
> CAREFULLY PUT ON ONE SIDE. HE LOOKS TO THE PIPER FOR
> APPROVAL TO BEGIN. THE PIPER NODS AND LEAVES.

ELDER
The Palace is ready
The hour stands aside
The wedding will take place
We await the Groom and Bride.

> THE FOLLOWING SCENE IS DONE IN MIME-DANCE TO MUSIC.
> DOORS OF BOTH HOUSES OPEN. THE KING STEPS FROM ONE,
> THE QUEEN FROM THE OTHER. THEY MARCH TO EACH OTHER
> PLACING THEIR HANDS ONE ON TOP OF EACH OTHER. THEY
> WALK TOWARDS THE WREATHS. ELIZABETH MARCHES FROM
> HER MOTHER'S HOUSE. THE COUPLE APPROACH THE ALTAR.
> TOWN ELDER PUTS A WREATH ON THE QUEEN'S HEAD. THE
> STONE-LIKE ALTAR COVERED WITH FLOWERS AND WREATHS
> IS CAREFULLY ARRANGED BY THE TOWN ELDER TO ALLOW
> THE KING & QUEEN TO KNEEL. TOWN ELDER BLESSES THEM,
> AS TOWNSPEOPLE ENTER AND ASSEMBLE. MUSIC BUILDS.

ELDER
The prayer is said
And you are wed.

> MUSIC CONTINUES AS TOWNSPEOPLE DANCE. SUDDENLY ELIZ-
> ABETH SCREAMS -- ALL LOOK IN HORROR.

ELIZABETH   The Rats -- the Rats -- they are here. They are
in the Palace. (SHE IS MESMERIZED BY FEAR) Vengeance! Vengeance!

> THE KING IS HOLDING THE QUEEN AND COVERING HER EYES.
> HE TOO FOR THE FIRST TIME IS AFRAID.

KING   We will hold back the Rats!! (HOLDING ON TIGHTLY TO HIS
CROWN)   My Crown! My Crown!
SPECIAL LIGHTING.

QUEEN   (DESTROYED)
Oh God, please help us to atone.
This sinful love the Fates bemoan.

> ELIZABETH TAKES HER MOTHER AND COMFORTS HER, WHILE
> THE KING STANDS THERE. EVERYTHING MOVES QUICKLY.

ELIZABETH   (TENDERLY)
Mother -- Mother pray be still.
The Fates cry vengeance with the Furies' Will!

> BLACKOUT   --   CURTAIN   --   END OF ACT TWO.

ACT THREE

THE PIPER AND HIS FRIEND COME DOWN THE AISLE PLAYING MUSIC AND DANCING AS THEY GO. THEY STOP AND DANCE AND PLAY WITH CHILDREN IN THE AUDIENCE UNTIL THEY REACH THE STAGE. THE CURTAINS OPEN ON A TABLEAU OF THE PREVIOUS SCENE, EVERYONE STILL FROZEN WITH FEAR. THE KING AND QUEEN SEE THE STRANGERS. THE KING IS SUSPIC-IOUS OF THE PLAYERS.

KING (RECOVERING SLIGHTLY) First the Rats and now these strange men. Who are you? Who has sent you? My sword is ready!! (HE STARTS TO PULL HIS SWORD)

PIPER (WITH REASSURANCE) Oh King of Hamelin cursed and plagued, I have come to rid Hamelin of the Rats.

KING PUTS BACK HIS SWORD WHEN PIPER SAYS "KING".

KING (DISTRUSTFUL) A Stranger! From nowhere!

SPECIAL LIGHTING.

PIPER
Try me -- see what I can do.
For by the ebbing tide
The Rats will follow side by side
And I will lead them to the sea
Where they will drown -- and you'll be free.

BOTH PLAYERS ENACT DROWNING OF RATS.

KING (MOCKINGLY) And how will they follow you?

PIPER By the pipe I play -- the tune I call.

KING (IRONICALLY) A Pied Piper will save us all? (LAUGHS)

PIPER (SERIOUSLY)
From a tiny seed, a tree grows on.
Laugh if you will and we'll be gone.

KING
(COMMANDINGLY) No. Stay.
Let us see what you can do.
And for this tune that you will play
Tell me the price that I must pay.

HE HOLDS ON TO HIS PURSE TIGHTLY. MUSIC.

PIPER
The price? I ask ten bags of gold
King Amon's sword and his robe of old
The Virgin forest untouched by you
Where I may start my house anew

And your sworn word, I and my children stay
Without harm in any way.

    END MUSIC.

KING   (CONNIVING)
Your price is fair -- and well agreed
The land is worthless for my need.
      (OMINOUSLY)
Now let us with this handshake pray
That you succeed on my Wedding Day.
If this is a jest -- a game you play
You will not live to end the day.

      (TO THE QUEEN)
Come now my Queen put grief aside
Remember today, you are my bride.

        TAKES HER ARM. ELIZABETH NOW LOOKS TO ORIN PLEAD-
        INGLY. HIS EYES BID HER TO STAY. THE KING AND QUEEN
        EXIT TO KING'S HOUSE. TOWNSPEOPLE EXIT. PLAYER 1
        REMAINS WITH ELIZABETH. ORIN BEGINS HIS PLAYING. THE
        TOWN ELDER LISTENS. IT IS ALMOST THE SAME TUNE AS
        BEFORE ONLY MORE MAGIC IN THE PLAYING. HE PUTS ON HIS
        TOWN CRIER'S HAT AS THE PIPER DISAPPEARS. WE HEAR HIS
        MUSIC AS THE TOWN CRIER DESCRIBES WHAT IS HAPPENING
        AND PLAYER 1 ENACTS ALONE WHAT TOWN CRIER SEES. ELIZ-
        ABETH IS OVERWHELMED WITH JOY.

CRIER
Now suddenly from everywhere
Comes a rumbling noise as if despair
Has taken wing and flies away
A dark cloud lifts this very day.
But closer, closer draws the sound
O cloud of light, the rats have found
The Piper's tune.
They run away from house and home
They leave the shops for streets to roam
Look, how they run -- look how they flee
They follow him down into the sea.
      (MUSIC REACHES CLIMAX HERE)
They drown; they are no more.

ELIZABETH
Oh Hamelin good is now in store
Heaven reward this Piper's call
Which saved Hamelin once and for all.

ELIZABETH, CRIER & PLAYER
Such happiness makes us weak
Our hearts decry our tongues to speak.

        TOWN CRIER LOOKS AROUND AT THE ALTAR, TOUCHES THE
        WREATHS. HE CALLS AS HE RINGS HIS BELL. ELIZABETH
        DANCES AROUND THE ALTAR WITH PLAYER 1.

CRIER
One o'clock and all is well
One o'clock and all is well.

BLACKOUT

SCENE TWO

AS IN PREVIOUS SCENE. KING, QUEEN, ELIZABETH, PLAYER 1 AND THE TOWN CRIER ARE ALL ON STAGE. THE FLOWERS REMAIN. THE MUSIC IS PLAYING AND EVERYONE IS DANCING IN AN ALMOST ABANDONED WAY. IT IS A GROUP DANCE, FESTIVE AND FILLED WITH JOY.

CRIER
Rejoice today -- oh, what a day!
Sing -- dance in every street.
Men - women -- children
Drink and eat.
Even fire and water -- old enemies

(TOWN CRIER BECOMES WATER -- GOOD. PLAYER 1 BECOMES FIRE -- EVIL. THEY BOTH ENACT THE FOLLOWING IMAGE)

Stirred in a blended brew
Make the bread to bake, and meat to stew.
Enchantment of sweet Spring seeping
Gentle fire of twilight sweeping
Black embers of nightime creeping
For such a twilight as this was never seen.
Hamelin from its Rats is clean.
Oh, celebrate!

(HE TWIRLS WITH THE MUSIC. DANCE CONTINUES EVEN THOUGH SPEECHES MAY STOP ONE PERSON -- OTHERS CARRY ON. AS HE SPEAKS, PLAYER 1 AND HE ENTWINE THEMSELVES TOGETHER AND CAN'T UNTWINE. THEY DANCE TOGETHER AS EVERYONE LAUGHS)

The dance of Spring -- we dance for you.
For life in Hamelin begins anew.

MUSIC CONTINUES EVEN GAYER. TOWN CRIER TAKES OFF HIS HAT AND PUTS ON A WREATH OF FLOWERS. HE DANCES HIS OWN DANCE AS THE KING, QUEEN, ELIZABETH AND PLAYER 1 DANCE ROUND HIM AND THE ALTAR. GRADUALLY THEY ARE ALL MOVING AROUND THE ALTAR, A HAPPY GROUP STILL FILLED WITH JOY AND DANCING WHEN THE PIED PIPER RETURNS. MUSIC STOPS.

SPECIAL LIGHTING.

PIPER   (BOWS)
My King -- My Lord -- my task is through.
Not a Rat in Hamelin is left to you.
And now give me my payment due.

KING   Payment? What payment?

PIPER
The virgin forest. Ten bags of gold.
Then King Amnon's sword and his robe of old.

KING
A deed that's done
And worth the doing
Asks no payment
Demands no pursuing.

EVERYONE REACTS WITH SHOCK.

PIPER
Am I to be dismissed -- alone?
Even dogs are rewarded with a bone.

QUEEN   (FEARFUL)
I beg you pay him his due
Or brooding night will blacken you.

KING   (TO PIPER)
Go, stranger -- leave these shores.
Else iron chains and death be yours.

EVERYONE LOOKING ON HAS BEEN SHOCKED INTO QUIET.
THEY CANNOT BELIEVE THAT JOY COULD BE SO SHORT-
LIVED. ATTEMPTS NOW AT REASON ARE BEING MADE.

CRIER
King, be merciful lest Hamelin bleed once more.
Stranger, Hamelin will give whatever you ask for.

PIPER
I thank all Hamelin
With this trusty sword. (HE TOUCHES PLAYER 1's SWORD)
But you, my King,
Owe me my reward.

KING
The King owes nothing for this day.
Beware your life -- now on your way.

ELIZABETH
Oh, Heavens will this story never end
Once I cried Vengeance and thought
Justice came instead, as friend.
Justice come back
You were not born to be entombed.
Atone our anguished cries
Cries of the doomed.

SHE STANDS WEEPING AND ALONE. EACH ONE STANDS ALONE
NOT KNOWING WHAT WILL HAPPEN.

THE SPEECHES FOLLOW QUICKLY ONE AFTER ANOTHER.

CRIER
King be merciful. Let our pleas be heard.
Think of Hamelin. Do not break your word.

KING
Wagging tongues keep still.
You have spoken against my will.

PIPER
If you refuse my payment due --
A curse far worse -- will fall on you.

KING   Villain -- demon -- your life is through.

> HE DRAWS HIS SWORD AND GOES TO THE PIPER MENACINGLY. BATTLE MUSIC BEGINS. THE PIPER DODGES THE BLOWS. IT IS ALL DONE IN MIME MOVEMENT. THE QUEEN HAS BEEN WATCHING WITH HORROR AS ELIZABETH WEEPS AND CALLS FOR HELP AT THE ALTAR. IN THE BATTLE THE PIPER'S HAT FALLS OFF. BOTH IN THE MUSIC AND MOVEMENT COMES A CLIMACTIC MOVEMENT -- A MOMENT OF RECOGNITION. THE QUEEN SEES THE WHOLE FACE OF THE PIPER FOR THE FIRST TIME AND RECOGNISES HER SON.

QUEEN   Orin -- Orin -- it is you!

> (SHE RUNS IN FRONT OF HIM PROTECTING HIM AS A SHIELD FROM THE SWORD OF THE KING)

Kill him and you kill me too!

KING
Stand aside, woman,
This is a task for men to do.

QUEEN   To shed blood -- and more blood. I will not let you.

> SHE STANDS FIRM. THE KING IS ENRAGED. ORIN HAS THREATENED HIS CROWN. HE LUNGES FORTH.

> THE MUSIC SUDDENLY STOPS. ALL ACTION STOPS AS PLAYER 1 GRABS THE KING'S SWORD. HE IS NO LONGER THE PLAYER. HE THROWS OFF HIS CAP.

PLAYER 1
Be thankful King
That I leave your head
For your sword will become
My Sceptre instead.

> (KING TRIES TO GET BACK HIS SWORD)

Just one step more, and you my Lord
Will see my Sceptre become a sword.
If there is blood foully shed
You'll bear witness for the dead.
I am a King from a Foreign land

(PUTS CROWN ON HIS HEAD)

With many armies at my command.
Orin has come back with me
To set all of Hamelin free.
The King's evil we already knew,
We'll not fight but reason with you.
And now with truth as my guide
I shall be judge as you are tried.
Assemble here -- this is a court
And high justice is our resort.
The Robes of Justice shall be placed on me.

(THE MUSIC STARTS AGAIN AS THE ROBE TAKEN FROM THE
PLAYER'S BAG IS PUT UPON HIM BY ORIN IN A PATTERNED
MOVEMENT SUGGESTING THE PAGEANTRY OF SUCH A
CEREMONY)

And the scales of justice for all to see.

(THE SCALES ARE PUT ON THE BACK OF THE ALTAR WHICH
NOW BECOMES THE SEAT OF JUSTICE. PLAYER 1 IS NOW THE
JUDGE WITH HIS CROWN, SCEPTRE AND ROBES)

Let the Furies and Fate here decide
That a dishonoured King and his Bride
Do rule the town of Hamelin
Once filled with pride,
Now full of sin.

(KING MOVES FORWARD BUT JUDGE'S STARE STOPS HIM. TO
TOWN CRIER)

You fearful citizens, watched the planting of this seed.
Yet did not pluck this evil weed.
At last to Hamelin returned its rightful heir

(ORIN AND THE KING STEP FORWARD. ORIN MOVES THE KING
BACK)

And delivered this town from plague and despair.
Yet for this the crown had no reward
Except a broken word and threat by sword.
Hear me and what I shall decree
How the scales will be balanced equally.
Pied Piper your tune you'll play
And all the children with you will march away.

(QUEEN AND TOWN CRIER GASP)

For he shall be the rightful king
Of a good new land from the beginning.
And it will be beyond compare
With love and laughter to fill the air.

(NOW POINTING TO KING, QUEEN AND TOWN CRIER)

And you in Hamelin who do remain
Will live out your lives in repentant pain.
But when you are gone, Hamelin will be no more.
And so will end evil on Hamelin's shore.

(THE KING STANDS DEFEATED AND ALONE)

Now Piper your tune begin to play
And Elizabeth too will march away.

QUEEN   (TO ORIN AND ELIZABETH)
No, no, I beg you both stay, only stay.

ORIN
Oh, Mother, would that you could come away.
But we must abide by the judgment of this day

HE KISSES HER AND THEN ELIZABETH KISSES HER.

QUEEN
I shall love you to the end of time.
Near or far, you are always mine.

KING   (TO QUEEN)
You married me against your will.
The marriage vows I will fulfil
If you would but have me still.

QUEEN LOOKS ON HIM WITH PITY AND NODS "YES" AS FOR
THE FIRST TIME HE TAKES HER TENDERLY BY THE ARM.

CRIER   (PLEADING)
Leave us but one -- one little try.
A crippled child would surely die
If forced to go so far away.
Please, I beg you, let Edward stay.

PLAYER 1   (AS JUDGE)
Your plea is granted
Your wish fulfilled
I now decree
That it be willed
But give him love that is fierce and strong
That feeds his life, his lifetime long.
And now, King, I return your sword.

ORIN
We begin our journey.
Farewell my lord.

ELIZABETH
We make some other land our home.

ORIN
A coming of age -- a growing glory.

ELIZABETH
A happy ending to our story.

END OF SPECIAL LIGHT. THE MUSIC ENDS. THE ACTORS TAKE
THEIR BOW IN PLACE.

THE PIPER THEN BEGINS TO PLAY HIS TUNE, LEAVING THE STAGE AND GOING THROUGH THE AUDIENCE. ELIZABETH AND PLAYER 1 JOIN HIM. TOGETHER THEY TAKE WITH THEM THE MAJORITY OF THE CHILDREN FROM THE AUDIENCE OUT INTO THE LOBBY. TOWN CRIER COMES FORWARD AND ADDRESSES THE AUDIENCE AS THE CHILDREN LEAVE. HE REPEATS THE FIRST SIX LINES OF THE FOLLOWING VERSE UNTIL THE CHILDREN HAVE LEFT THE THEATRE AND ARE IN THE LOBBY.

CRIER   (TO CHILDREN)
Oh children -- children -- follow -- follow
Follow the piper
As does the swallow
The song he plays
Is sweeter still
Than the thrush or lark
Whose notes sound shrill.

          (TO ADULTS ALONE IN THE THEATRE)
Now that all the children go
Good friends let us on them bestow
Blessings of a newborn age
Not death -- not war -- not even rage
But crown our song with sounds of love
For the newborn age give them peace -- a dove.

                    END OF PLAY.

TWO CASTLE WALLS - ONE FOR THE KING - ONE FOR THE QUEEN

'HAMLIN' PAINTED
ON BACK CLOTH

A STONE BENCH
BECOMES THE ALTAR

COSTUMES

THE RATS

THE PIED PIPER AND PLAYER TWO

COSTUMES

QUEEN

ELIZABETH

KING AEGIS

PLAYER 1

PLAYER 2

the
BIRthday
of the
INfanta

BY BLANCHE MARVIN

THE BIRTHDAY OF THE INFANTA

King Ferdinand of Spain

Queen Maria, his French Queen

Duchess Isabel of Aragon, wife of Don Pedro

Don Pedro, Prince of Aragon - brother to the King

Infanta Maria, Daughter of Ferdinand and Maria

The Dwarf

Grand Inquisitor

> Children
> Ladies-in-Waiting
> Courtiers

Place: Spain - Madrid and Aragon

Act I

1. Don Pedro's throne room in his Palace in Aragon
2. Corridor and Ballroom, of Ferdinand's Palace, Madrid
3. Don Pedro's throne room
4. Hallway in Don Pedro's Palace
5. Bedroom of King Ferdinand's Palace

Act 2

Ballroom of King Ferdinand's Palace

Time: 1550

Please note that in Act I, despite the five scenes, the Ballroom and its corridor are the main set. Don Pedro's throne room can be in the corridor with curtains to change the scene. Don Pedro's hallway can be down stage, blacking out the set or in front of the front curtain. The royal bedroom needs only the royal bed set in the ballroom with lights focused on the bed and the immediate area.

The Birthday of the Infanta is directly related to the Spanish classical drama and is based on Oscar Wilde's fairy tale which in turn is based on a true Spanish story. The dancing is part of the play and therefore not a musical number. Flamenco as well as French Baroque music can be used in the background. The movement of the adults is precise except for the French Queen who should be contrasted in lightness. Unlike the English classics there is no humour through comic characters in this story. The dwarf can be a small young actor but the face must be large and ugly. Its theme is about the corruption of power possible even in a child. It is also about rigidity of structures and authority as it destroys regardless of motive. The adaptation is straightforward - a Spanish story in classical 16th century Spanish style in design, music and movement.

Pictures and drawings are indexed in the back of the book.

ACT ONE

> THE PALACE OF DON PEDRO, DUKE OF ARAGON AND BROTHER TO
> THE KING OF SPAIN. HE IS TALL, DARK, ARROGANT AND
> CALCULATING. HE IS SEATED ON HIS THRONE TALKING TO HIS
> WIFE, THE DUCHESS OF ANDALUSIA. SHE IS A WELL ROUNDED
> WOMAN OF GREAT AMBITION BUT SOFTER THAN HER HUSBAND.
> THEY ARE ELEGANTLY DRESSED AS BEFITS THEIR STATION.
> THE YEAR IS 1550, AT THE HEIGHT OF THE SPANISH INFLUENCE
> AND POWER AS THE MOST CIVILISED KINGDOM OF EUROPE. THE
> THRONE IS SET CENTRE STAGE. THE ROOM IS ORNATE. THE
> DUKE IS ALONE WITH THE DUCHESS.

DON PEDRO Wife.

> IRRITATED, AS THE DUCHESS IS NOT LISTENING. SHE IS PAC-
> ING BACK AND FORTH.

Are you not the wife of Don Pedro? Answer your Lord!

> DUCHESS STOPS - LOOKS AT DON PEDRO - BUT OBVIOUSLY NOT
> PAYING MUCH ATTENTION.

DUCHESS Indeed I am -- or so I thought for these last fifteen years. Could it be someone other than myself is your wife? Now let me see -- (LOOKS AROUND) No -- I see no one else. It must be I who am your wife.

DON PEDRO You will not jest. Remember your place and who you are. (GRABS HER ARM SWIFTLY) This is my palace and we are in Aragon - in Spain. We are not foolish as the French with oohs and aahs - nor barbarous as the English with swearing and course laughter. We are Spaniards - proud and obedient.

> HE HAS BOTH HER ARMS BEHIND HER BACK.

DUCHESS Ah, yes, husband. We are Spaniards. Release my arms, I beg you.

DON PEDRO We are proud and obedient.

DUCHESS We are proud and obedient. I beg you -- release my arms. You are hurting me.

DON PEDRO I meant to hurt. Remember the pain whenever you think to ignore your Lord.

DUCHESS Someone might see us. It does not befit a Duke and Duchess to be seen in their Court in this way.

> DON PEDRO RELEASES HER.

DON PEDRO Duchess of Andalusia, and Aragon, wife of Don Pedro, Prince of Aragon, are you now prepared to listen to serious news -- or will you continue with your French games?

DUCHESS   I am all ears, my husband. What serious news do you have for me?

DON PEDRO   What other news is there but my brother -- the King of Spain -- and his foolish new Queen, that French wench.

DUCHESS   That "French wench" as you call her is our Queen and a Princess in her own right from the Court of Versailles.

DON PEDRO   Don't take me for the fool. I know full well about our Queen and from where she comes. I care nothing for the Queen. It is Spain that concerns me. News has arrived that England's ships are spanning the seas to the East. Where are the Spanish ships? Close to our shores! Our King is too in love, to ponder about such important matters of State. The blue eyes and sighs of his Queen are all that interest him.

DUCHESS   Spain is in no danger. Let the King enjoy his love.

DON PEDRO   Danger! We rule the world! Where will our strength lie -- if not with the King?

DUCHESS   What do you propose to do? You must have a plan?

DON PEDRO   I have invited my brother and his Queen to our Palace, here. Then I will speak to him about his duties as King.

DUCHESS   And will the King of Spain listen to the Prince of Aragon?

DON PEDRO   He will listen. I command the most powerful Duchy in the Kingdom.

DUCHESS   Will the King come to Aragon? Why not go to Madrid and speak with your brother at the Royal Palace!

DON PEDRO   Foolish woman -- the King must visit me in Aragon to see my strength!

DUCHESS   And what of the new-born Princess, the baby Infanta? Do you wish her presence in Court?

DON PEDRO   The Infanta has little to do with us at the moment. It is the King that concerns me.

DUCHESS   Very well, my Lord. I will go and prepare the Palace for the arrival of our King and Queen.

　　　　(STARTS TO LEAVE, BUT RETURNS)

I would have enjoyed the Infanta's coming.

DON PEDRO   There is no time for children.

DUCHESS   There could have been.

DON PEDRO   There will never be!

DUCHESS   Who will be your heir?

DON PEDRO   Wait and see!

DUCHESS   May I take my leave?

DON PEDRO   Take your leave. You should approve the royal visit.
          (SHE EXITS)

The fool -- he makes a mockery of the Spanish Empire! Our
whole kingdom can crumble and he will only worry if the French
cream puff drops an eyelid. What will become of Spain with such
a King?

SONG: **TO BE A KING**

What does it mean to be?
To be king of glorious Spain?
To war on land, to war on sea
To hold down the greed of our nobility
To collect the tax to pay for this
To have strength of mind to say all this
That is what it means to be
To be King of glorious Spain.

To fight the battle, win or lose
To have the generals and staff to choose
To see the crops grow full and strong
And keep the people where they belong
To fill the Crown's purse with silver and gold
And make our goods be bought and sold
To set the laws and see them through
To conquer lands that might conquer you.

To build castles that show power and wealth
That also have treasures to glorify oneself
That's what it means to be
To be King of glorious Spain.
Where does my brother, the King of Spain
War on land, war on sea?
Where does my brother, the King of Spain
Hold down the greedy nobility?

Or fight the battle, win or lose,
Have the generals and staff to choose,
Keep the people where they belong,
Collect the tax; see the crops are strong
Fill the Crown's purse with silver and gold
Make our goods be bought and sold
Set the laws and see them through
Conquer lands that might conquer you.
These things my brother will never do!!
Though King of Spain, he'll sit and coo

The sweet nothings to his new Queen bride
Who now consumes all his Spanish pride.
Where is the King, that was meant to be?
Where is the glory for Spain to see?

He lives here within and not on the throne
For glorious Spain, make the crown my own
For Glorious Spain, for Glorious Spain
I'll kill the King, make the Crown my own.

CURTAIN

SCENE TWO

THE PALACE OF THE KING AND QUEEN OF SPAIN IN MADRID, SET
IN THE HALLWAY OR WAITING ROOM TO THE BALLROOM AND IN
THE BALLROOM. IT IS GRAND, DECORATIVE, ALMOST MOORISH IN
DESIGN. THE WALLS OF THE BALLROOM ARE COVERED WITH
ENORMOUS MIRRORS. CRYSTAL CHANDELIERS ADD GLITTER TO
THE MIRRORS.

THE LADIES-IN-WAITING, ELEGANTLY GROOMED, ARE GOSSIPING
IN THE WAITING ROOM AS THEY PLAY THEIR COURTLY GAME OF
WHAT WE CALL SHUFFLE-BOARD.

1ST LADY   What do you think of the queen's golden locks --
Lady Dolores?

2ND LADY   (Lady Dolores) The beauties of Castile have locks
as fair. Our King thinks the grass is greener in someone else's
garden.

3RD LADY   They say the Queen is a mere child. Should Spain be
ruled by children?

1ST LADY   Spain is ruled by a King. (LAUGHS) Or so they say!

2ND LADY   The only child -- is the Infanta.

3RD LADY   The Infanta is Spanish. At least she'll never become
a French bride.

1ST LADY   Meanwhile, Spain has a French Queen, Lady Dolores.

3RD LADY   And you, Lady Dolores, lost a Spanish King.

2ND LADY   I'll learn some of the gay French manners and maybe
win back my King.

3RD LADY   You treasure the happiness of the King and Queen.

1ST LADY   All Spain treasures their happiness.

2ND LADY   Sooner or later the King will have to bend to the will
of Spain!!

3RD LADY Move quickly -- here come the lovesick couple.

THEY EXIT AS THE KING AND QUEEN ENTER. THE KING LOOKS ABOUT AND IS RELIEVED TO FIND NO ONE THERE. THEY GLIDE DIRECTLY INTO THE BALLROOM.

KING Where else could we be alone, but in the Grand Ballroom when there is no ball.

QUEEN Is cold ballroom when no music and dancing feet. Come to garden.

KING Eyes peer from everywhere upon us. There is no quiet nook, even in the garden. From what Paradise did your golden locks fall?

QUEEN Where you come from? No from Spain.

KING I look at you and wonder. I know where you came from -- from...

QUEEN France.

KING No -- heaven.

QUEEN Today no Queen -- no King. Maria and Ferdinand. Just man, just woman.

KING But we are both -- King and Queen. Man and woman ruling Spain and in love. What more could we ask?

QUEEN Spain love King -- but hate Queen. "French woman", they say. No one love Queen.

KING I know of one -- a King who loves her.

QUEEN I want France.

KING France made you and therefore I love France. But Spain needs you.

QUEEN I need you -- but not Spain.

KING Are you unhappy here?

QUEEN No -- no. I not be without you. I live tip of the world with you.

KING And I with you.

QUEEN I not speak proper to explain.

KING I can understand everything you say.

QUEEN No else in Court understand me. I learn speak Spanish.

KING   It doesn't matter whether the Court understands you or not.

SONG   **THE LOOK OF LOVE**

KING
With the look of love that is in your eyes
You need no words, the heart alone speaks.
That look -- those eyes
Are words I recognize.
It's love, it's love that spells around you
Now I have found you
Now I have found you.

QUEEN
My heart has heard
Your heart speak.

KING
My eyes of love
Your eyes seek.

QUEEN & KING
In the language (of) love there must be no bounds
No far-off countries, no foreign grounds
That look - those eyes
Are words I recognize.
It's joy, it's joy that flashes round you
Now I have found you
Now I have found you
Now I have found you.

> THE GRAND INQUISITOR ENTERS THE BALLROOM. HE IS AN
> OLD MAN -- SLIGHTLY FOOLISH. HE IS OUT OF BREATH FOR
> HAVING SEARCHED FOR THE KING.

INQUISITOR   Oh there -- at last -- I have found the King!

KING   And is the King so difficult to find?

INQUISITOR   Indeed he is. What King would hide himself away in
the Grand Ballroom with his Queen?

KING   A very special King only would do such a thing.

INQUISITOR   But why choose the Ballroom?

KING   The better for you to find us, Grand Inquisitor.

QUEEN   Why to find? What reason?

INQUISITOR   A reason? Oh me, yes. Of course. News has been
brought from Aragon. Your brother Don Pedro awaits your arrival.

KING   Must we accept this invitation?

INQUISITOR I have delivered the message myself because I feared you would refuse the messenger. You cannot refuse. You cannot offend Don Pedro. He would be offended by any delay.

KING   Then we must prepare for the journey.

INQUISITOR The Duchy of Aragon has the greatest wealth. Don Pedro upholds the very heart of Spain. He can lead armies against you. Take care!

QUEEN   We not go to Aragon!

KING   Yes, we must. But there is nothing to fear. My brother is a man of great passion, but he would not harm the Crown!

QUEEN   What of Baby Infanta?

INQUISITOR I shall remain in Madrid. The child is safe. But beware in Aragon.

KING   The Infanta is to be under constant guard. And that is an order from the King.

INQUISITOR I will stand guard here in Madrid.

BLACKOUT

SCENE THREE

> CASTLE OF DON PEDRO. SAME AS SCENE 1, ONLY THRONE IS MORE DECORATED. THE MEMBERS OF THE COURT STAND STILL AND FORMAL AS THEY WAIT THE ARRIVAL OF THE KING AND QUEEN. THE DUCHESS IS NERVOUS AS SHE QUIETLY TALKS TO DON PEDRO.

DUCHESS I know there is more to your plan than what you have told me. You are plotting something against the King.

DON PEDRO Silence -- wife! Your whining will disturb their visit. There is no plot. Just be a gracious hostess.

DUCHESS I am always gracious and cautious with you, my Lord.

DON PEDRO Alphonso, remember -- the King is to be seated slowly on the throne. It is very important we seat the King. Wait for me to carry the cloak. It must not touch anyone but the King.

DUCHESS What have you done to the cloak?

DON PEDRO Nothing! Royal robes should only be touched by royalty. Now keep to your place -- else you might lose it forever.

73

DUCHESS (WHISPERING) You will -- kill -- the King?

DON PEDRO (FIERCELY) Silence!

> TRUMPETS ANNOUNCE THE KING AND QUEEN'S ENTRANCE. THEY FORMALLY ENTER THE ROOM WITH ENTOURAGE. THE DUKE, DUCHESS AND ALL HIS COURT PARTAKE OF THE FORMAL PLACEMENT, DONE AS A COURT DANCE. THE BROTHERS KISS ON BOTH CHEEKS AS TRADITIONALLY DONE. THE KING FOLLOWS ALL THE CEREMONIAL RULES EXCEPT WHEN DON PEDRO AND ALPHONSO TRY TO SEAT HIM ON THE THRONE. THE KING, INSTEAD, PERSONALLY SEATS THE QUEEN UPON THE THRONE. THIS IS HIS WAY OF SHOWING DON PEDRO THE QUEEN'S POSITION. DON PEDRO IS IN A CONTROLLABLE FURY. THEN HE BECOMES EXPRESSIONLESS. AN ALMOST MASK-LIKE QUALITY COMES OVER HIS FACE AS HE CONTINUES THE CEREMONY. HE MUST CONTINUE. THE DUCHESS IS AWARE THAT SOMETHING TERRIBLE HAS GONE WRONG. SHE NOW STEPS BESIDE DON PEDRO, WHO CAREFULLY PUSHES HER AWAY. DON PEDRO, AT FIRST HESITATES WITH THE CLOAK THEN GOES TOWARD THE KING TO PUT THE CLOAK OVER HIM. ALPHONSO FOLLOWS. BUT THE KING REFUSES THE CLOAK AND POINTS TO THE QUEEN. DON PEDRO STANDS LOOKING. THE KING STANDS FIRM AND POINTS TO THE QUEEN AS ALPHONSO ASSISTS HIM. THE KING ONCE AGAIN POINTS TO THE ROBE -- IT MUST BE CLASPED CLOSED. DON PEDRO OBEYS. AS SOON AS THE CLOAK IS CLOSED, THE QUEEN GASPS, STRUGGLES FOR BREATH AND FAINTS. THE KING RUSHES TO HER SIDE.

KING What is it, my love? Don Pedro, call the physician!

> DON PEDRO RUSHES OUT.

QUEEN No -- breath. (STILL IN FAINT)

KING Help me remove the cloak! Give her air!

> DUCHESS RUNS TO HELP THE KING.

DUCHESS Don't touch the cloak, my King! Just keep the Queen's head moving. Alphonso, remove the cloak. Hold it by the collar -- as you did before. Do not touch the royal robe -- only the collar.

> ALPHONSO REMOVES THE ROBE OR CLOAK, HOLDING IT EXACTLY THE WAY HE HELD IT BEFORE, AND EXITS.

> THE DUCHESS FRANTICALLY TRIES TO REVIVE THE QUEEN WITH THE KING'S HELP. THE COURT GO BACK TO THEIR PLACES LIKE MACHINES. THE KING KEEPS MOVING THE QUEEN'S HEAD FROM SIDE TO SIDE.

KING Wake up, my sweet. Wake up -- please, wake up. Please -- please wake up.

CURTAIN

SCENE FOUR

A HALLWAY IN DON PEDRO'S PALACE, A FEW MONTHS LATER. THIS CAN BE IN FRONT OF THE CURTAIN. IT IS LATE AT NIGHT. THE DUCHESS IS QUIETLY STEALING AWAY FROM THE PALACE, FOLLOWED BY A LADY-IN-WAITING CARRYING HER BAGS. ONE BAG SLIPS AND FALLS, MAKING A LOUD SOUND.

DUCHESS   Fool -- fool -- we may be discovered!

LADY   I am sorry, my Lady.

DUCHESS   That will not help us with my Lord, Don Pedro!

DON PEDRO APPEARS SUDDENLY. DUCHESS SCREAMS AND JUMPS BACK.

DON PEDRO   Are you going -- somewhere, without my consent, my Duchess?

DUCHESS   Oh -- oh, it's only you, Don Pedro! Go to the carriage with my bags, Juanita. (SHE EXITS WITH BAGS)

DON PEDRO   Betrayal to Don Pedro can mean imprisonment. What have you to say for yourself, Duchess, that can save you?

DUCHESS   I do not need to save myself. I have nothing to hide. Though I planned to leave without your consent, it is urgent that I go to Madrid and stay with the King at the Palace. If one of us does not appear, it will surely be thought that we are responsible for the Queen's illness. After all these months, she is now dying.

DON PEDRO   The Queen has a fatal illness. No one knows what it is. Oh -- my brother is more fool than I ever dreamed! To seat a Queen upon a throne meant for a King!

DUCHESS   I hear what the people say. We must appease and comfort the King. I must go to Madrid for our safety.

DON PEDRO   You admit to our guilt!

DUCHESS   No - never! The grief over the Queen's illness is then shared by us all. I would never say a word to the King about the poison.

DON PEDRO   You know nothing --about any poison.

DUCHESS   I am your wife. You can trust me.

DON PEDRO   I trust no one. It cannot be proved that I harmed the Queen.

DUCHESS   I know the cloak contained poison. I know! The King knows it as well. It may have been the clasp. I'm not sure. But you meant it for your brother.

DON PEDRO   If all of this is so clear -- why am I not imprisoned? Why is there suddenly -- danger?

DUCHESS   The King has never left the Queen's side. Once she dies he may then seek revenge. I must be there to protect us!!

DON PEDRO   My brother's revenge? I could crush him with my army! It is only for the sake of the people that I do not!

DUCHESS   Then let me go for the sake of our people. They must not think you hurt the King -- or Queen.

DON PEDRO   How long can his broken heart beat after the Queen dies? Very well, you may go. But when the Queen dies, you will return; or else I march with my army to Madrid, and take you as prisoner.

DUCHESS   I will return. You have my word. Goodbye.

DON PEDRO   A good -- journey.

>   HE WATCHES HER LEAVE.
>   CURTAIN

SCENE FIVE

>   THE KING'S CASTLE IN MADRID. IT IS THE BEDROOM OF THE QUEEN. THE QUEEN IS DYING. THE KING KNEELS BY HER BEDSIDE. THE INFANTA LIES IN HER CRADLE. THE GRAND INQUISITOR PRESIDES OVER THE DEATH PRAYERS. THE LADIES-IN-WAITING SURROUND THE QUEEN'S BED PRAYING WITH THE INQUISITOR. THE DUCHESS PRAYS WITH THE LADIES, GOING BACK AND FORTH TO THE INFANTA. THE QUEEN LIES IN HER ROYAL BED AND SPEAKS GENTLY.

QUEEN   Ferdinand.

KING   Save yourself. Do not speak. I am here, Maria. I am always here.

QUEEN   Ba-by --

KING   She is here. Safe and sound. Rest. Just rest.

QUEEN   Protect - Baby --

KING   You will get well.

QUEEN   Protect Infanta till twelve --

KING   I will protect her. She will grow up to be Queen.

INQUISITOR   (TO KING) Join us in prayer.

KING   I will not pray at her death. I will not.

INQUISITOR My son, you must accept God's will.

KING   This is not God's will! She is dying instead of me.

INQUISITOR Delay such thoughts. Help her now to die in peace.

KING   She will not die --

QUEEN   Infanta - till twelve --

KING   You mustn't go. You must live.

QUEEN   Don Pedro till twelve --

  KING STOPS HER BY CALMLY STROKING HER HEAD.

ACT ONE FINALE: DEATH SONG - 'IF YOU GO AWAY"

KING
If you go away on this summer's day
Then you will take the summer away
The birds will sigh
The clouds will cry.
And flowers will surely die
If you go away
If you go away.

But,
If you stay, on this Summer's day
The dark clouds will drift away
The birds will fly
High in the sky
And flowers will never die
If you only stay
If you only stay

If you go away, on this Summer's day
Then I am left with greedy prey

  QUEEN DIES. THE KING LOOKS AT HER. THE DUCHESS WEEPS.

The empty look upon your face
Shows me your soul has left this place
And time for me will pass too slow
Until I find our next hello.
You've gone away on this summer's day

And taken all my summers away
For you cannot stay
No, you cannot stay.
No, you cannot stay.

DUCHESS   Queen Maria is dead. Infanta Maria lives.

  DUCHESS HANDS THE INFANTA INTO THE KING'S ARMS.
  END OF ACT ONE

SCENE ONE

MORE THAN ELEVEN YEARS LATER. IN THE BALLROOM AT THE PALACE IN MADRID. THE SAME AS ACT ONE EXCEPT FOR DECORATIONS STREWN ABOUT, WHICH ARE TO BE MOUNTED FOR THE INFANT'S BIRTHDAY PARTY. SHE IS TO BE 12.

THE DUCHESS IS PRESENT AND PLAYING WITH THE INFANTA, WHO LOOKS EXACTLY LIKE HER MOTHER WITH BLUE EYES AND GOLDEN LOCKS. (THE ACTRESS PLAYING THE QUEEN PLAYS THE INFANTA). THE GRAND INQUISITOR IS DOZING AWAY ON HIS SUPPOSED WATCH OVER THE INFANTA. THE INFANTA IS VERY EXCITED OVER THE PARTY.

INFANTA   Quickly -- quickly dear Aunt, finish closing the buttons on my dress.

DUCHESS   I don't think we'll have the party, after all. You're much too grown up for such childish things.

INFANTA   My birthday is not childish!

DUCHESS   Then why not be truly grown-up and have a grand State Dinner?

INFANTA   Oh no -- no. With all those old men who only cough -- but never speak. Oh no -- dear, dear Duchess, I shall make you a Marquesa if we have my Birthday Party.

DUCHESS   Very well, that seems to be an excellent reason for a Birthday Party.

        (SHE LAUGHS. THE INFANTA JOINS HER)
Twelve, already.

INFANTA   Have you known me all of my life?

DUCHESS   Yes, all of your life.

INFANTA   Was I always beautiful?

DUCHESS   You were a beautiful baby.

INFANTA   (STAMPING HER FOOT) I am beautiful now!

DUCHESS   A Spanish Queen-to-be does not stamp her foot.

INFANTA   But I am very cross with you.

DUCHESS   Then speak quietly and stand straight.

INFANTA   There I am standing straight and I will stamp my foot. (SHE STAMPS HER FOOT WITH GRACE)

DUCHESS   I think that I am not wanted here in Madrid. The time has come for me to return to Aragon.

INFANTA   No -- I command you to stay and help me with my birthday.

DUCHESS   Only the King can command me.

INFANTA   Then I will ask the King.

DUCHESS   There is a much easier way to ask. A magic word will do as well.

INFANTA   Then tell me the magic word.

DUCHESS   Please!

INFANTA   (ALL SMILES) Please stay.

DUCHESS   That's much better, but that is only the beginning. Why should I please stay?

THE INFANTA SUDDENLY RUNS INTO HER ARMS.

INFANTA   Because I love you -- as if you were my mother.

DUCHESS   Then I shall stay. But you must remember to behave as though I were your mother. You are not to stamp your foot.

INFANTA   Shall I tell you a secret?

DUCHESS   I love secrets.

INFANTA   In all of Spain, there is only you that I love!

DUCHESS   And what of your father, the King?

INFANTA   I can't love someone who really isn't there!

DUCHESS   But he loves you.

INFANTA   He loves only my mother and she died a long time ago.

DUCHESS   This shall be a happy day. No sad thoughts. Shall we hang the decorations?

INFANTA   The footmen will come soon to do it.

DUCHESS   (STARTS TO HANG THEM) I think these flowers look so lovely here.

INFANTA   They are beautiful. (SHE HELPS) You have always come to Madrid to see me, but I have never been to Aragon.

DUCHESS   There are no rooms for children. Besides I love to

79

come and visit you.

> THE KING HAS ENTERED. HE WATCHES THEM AS THEY HANG
> THE FLOWERS. HERE IS AN OLDER KING, LOOKING MUCH OLD-
> ER THAN HE ACTUALLY IS. THERE IS ALSO A DEEP CHANGE
> IN CHARACTER. HE IS QUIET, WITHDRAWN AND NEVER SPEAKS
> DIRECTLY TO ANYONE. HE LOOKS A SICK MAN.

KING   Maria, child --

INFANTA   Oh -- Father, you frightened me.

KING   What are you doing?

INFANTA   Hanging decorations.

KING   Is that what the Infanta is taught to do these days?

DUCHESS   It was my suggestion. I just thought it would be pleasant, my King, to --

KING   I see you have arrived for the Infanta's twelfth birthday.

DUCHESS   I have come for every birthday.

KING   Yes. Indeed, you have.

INFANTA   I couldn't have a birthday without my Aunt -- ah -- the Duchess. Papa -- will you stay to wish me Happy Birthday?

KING   I wish you happy birthday every day of your life. Are the entertainers coming?

INFANTA   Oh yes. There will be clowns, and jugglers, and bears, and dancers from all over the world. Oh, it is going to be very exciting!

KING   Good.

INFANTA   Is something wrong? You look at me strangely?

KING   You look more and more like your mother -- with each new birthday.

INFANTA   Do you like my new dress? It is my birthday dress.

KING   It is lovely. As lovely as those golden locks.

INFANTA   Will you come to the party?

KING   Of course I shall come.

INFANTA   My twelfth birthday is very special.

SONG: MY TWELFTH BIRTHDAY

INFANTA
Today is my birthday
I am 12, you see
Because it's my birthday
Spain belongs to me.

Everywhere from far and near
My subjects will come
And I shall appear
No more a child
No more Maria Infanta
I shall only appear
As Queen Maria Santa.

We'll have clowns and acrobats
And dogs and bears
We'll play bull fight games
And dance in pairs.
We'll be very gay
And laugh out loud
I think 12th birthdays
Deserve a crowd.

          (SHE DANCES ROUND)

Today is my birthday
May it never end
Today is my birthday
The world is my friend.

KING   I'm afraid **even grown-ups must have dinner. It is** time
for yours.

INFANTA   Please, dear Aunt, come and join me.

KING   I think not. Queens very often eat alone.

INFANTA   Please papa -- just for my birthday.

KING   There are some serious matters I must discuss with
the Duchess.

INFANTA   Since I am Queen, I may give a command -- and my
command is --

KING   To go now to dinner. Grand Inquisitor --

INFANTA   Then I shall eat alone.

          EXITS WITH GREAT DIGNITY. GRAND INQUISITOR WAKES UP
          SUDDENLY AND FOLLOWS THE INFANTA.

KING   I warn you and Don Pedro that the Infanta will be
guarded every moment. My brother will never harm that child.

81

DUCHESS   He does not wish to harm the Infanta. You forget that I love her too.

KING   False love. Win her confidence. Then she is easy catch for the kill. No Duchess, I am no longer deceived.

DUCHESS   There is no deception. She is like the child I never had. I will protect her as much as you.

KING   Then why does Don Pedro come to the Palace?

DUCHESS   To escort my return to Aragon. My visits are usually delayed in Madrid. The Prince can only be sure of my swift return by bringing me home himself.

KING   It is an official visit and all Spain will know he attended. One false move and all Spain will know that too.

DUCHESS   He comes as a well-wisher -- to see his niece. Is that so treacherous an act?

KING   Don Pedro comes to wish a child a happy birthday! No. No. He may come to kill me -- or to kill the Infanta, but not to visit. The child can now be Queen of Spain and even she knows it!

GRAND INQUISITOR RE-ENTERS.

INQUISITOR   Let there be peace for the sake of the child.

KING   There is no peace here. You must seek that in your monastery -- but not in the Palace!

INQUISITOR   Go -- dine with the child. She sits alone, as always.

KING   The Infanta alone? You know my orders!

INQUISITOR   The guards are there. But she has no companions.

KING   I must go to my chambers to prepare for the birthday and my brother's arrival.

DUCHESS   Dear God -- let the child survive all this!

CURTAIN

SCENE TWO

THE BALLROOM IS NOW COMPLETE AND RESPLENDENT IN ITS DECORATIONS. THE WHOLE SCENE IS DONE LIKE A DANCE. COURT MUSIC. EACH GROUP ENTERS WITH THE SAME FORMALITY OF MOVEMENT. FIRST, THE MEMBERS OF THE COURT. THEY GO CAREFULLY TO THEIR PLACE. THE DUCHESS AND GRAND INQUISITOR ENTER NEXT. THE GRAND INQUISITOR EXITS WHEN THE DUCHESS IS IN PLACE.

THEN COME THE YOUNG ARISTOCRATIC CHILDREN. THEIR MOVEMENTS ARE AS RIGID, PRECISE AND CONTROLLED AS THE ADULTS. THEY GO TO THEIR PLACES. AT LAST THE INFANTA ENTERS WITH THE GRAND INQUISITOR. SHE IS PROUD AND NOBLE AS A SPANISH QUEEN. HER DRESS IS COMPLETE WITH CROWN, COLLAR AND JEWELS AS SHE IS SEATED ON THE QUEEN'S THRONE. THE KING FINALLY ENTERS AND SITS UPON HIS THRONE. HE ACKNOWLEDGES THE ENTIRE COURT. THEN LOOKS TO THE INFANTA.

KING   It is your day -- my Maria. You have come of age. And now before you are too old, let the games begin.

THE BULL FIGHT MUSIC STARTS AS THE YOUNG BOYS ABANDON THEMSELVES AND BECOME IMPASSIONED BULL FIGHTERS, USING THEIR CLOAKS TO TAUNT THE BULLS WHO ARE PLAYED BY THE BOYS WAVING STICKS WITH BULL'S HEADS ON THEM. THE GIRLS DISPLAY AS MUCH VIOLENCE IN THEIR CALLING TO THE BOYS AND WAVING THEIR HANDKERCHIEFS. ONE GIRL PARTICIPATES WITH THE BOYS USING HER HANDKERCHIEF AS A FLAG FOR THE BULL. SHE IS PULLED BACK BY ONE OF THE OTHER GIRLS INTO PLACE. THIS IS ALL DONE AS A DANCE AND ENDS WITH THE KILLING OF THE BULLS TO THE GIRLS' CHEERS.

THE INFANTA IS AS INVOLVED AS EVERY OTHER CHILD THERE. THE KING LOOKS TOWARDS HER AND SEES HER VIOLENCE AS SHE TRIES TO KILL A BULL IN MIME-LIKE MOVEMENT. HE IS DISTURBED. THE CHILDREN GO BACK TO THEIR PLACES.

KING   Now for the entertainers? Is that not right Grand Inquisitor?

INQUISITOR   Yes, my King. They are waiting.

INFANTA   The Bears -- the bears will come first!

THE BEARS COME TUMBLING IN. THEY ARE LIFE-SIZE PUPPETS. ONE OF THEM IS AN ACTOR DRESSED AS A BEAR AND PERFORMS WITH THEM. THE ARABIAN DANCERS, FLAMENCO DANCERS, CLOWNS, CHINESE DANCERS, CIRCUS PERFORMERS, TURKISH DANCERS, TUMBLERS, BALLET DANCER ON HORSE-BACK, ETC., ENTER ONE AFTER THE OTHER. MUSIC AND PERFORMANCES BUILD. PUPPETS MAY BE USED THROUGHOUT. THEY ARE LIFESIZE AND INTERMINGLED ALWAYS WITH THE LIVE ACTOR. THE STAGE IS DARKENED SO THAT ONLY THE PERFORMERS ARE SEEN IN MULTI-LIGHTING. THE EFFECT MUST BE SENSATIONAL, ENDING WITH A PARADE OF ALL THE PERFORMERS AND THEN THEIR EXIT.

THE LIGHTS COME UP FULL AS THE EXCITED CHILDREN APPLAUD AND APPLAUD. IT IS THEN THAT DON PEDRO MAKES HIS DRAMATIC ENTRANCE. ALONGSIDE HIM IS A COLOURFUL DWARF, WHO TUMBLES TO THE FEET OF THE INFANTA. APPLAUSE FOR THE PARADE STOPS IMMEDIATELY UPON THEIR ENTRANCE.

EXCITEMENT BEGINS AGAIN WITH THE DWARF. HE DOES A DANCE TO THE FOLLOWING SPEECH AIMED AT THE INFANTA.

DWARF   Birthday greetings from Aragon -- (HE TURNS) from Granada -- from Seville -- from Toledo -- from Barcelona -- from Malaga -- from Cadiz -- from Valencia -- from Andorra -- Spain is at your feet. (HE TUMBLES TO HER FEET)

INFANTA   Spain thanks you. Oh Uncle, you have brought me the best present I have ever had!

KING   Don Pedro has arrived. Your lady waits for you.

DON PEDRO KNEELS BEFORE THE KING AND KISSES HIS HAND. THEN BOWS TO THE INFANTA AND KISSES HER HAND.

DON PEDRO   Happy Birthday Infanta Maria.

(HE THEN GOES TO THE DUCHESS)

My Lady.

DUCHESS   My Lord, you have surprised us with your thoughtful gift.

DON PEDRO   It is only once in a lifetime that a Queen comes of age.

DUCHESS   An Infanta.

DON PEDRO   A Queen.

DUCHESS   (ASIDE TO DON PEDRO)   What are you plotting?

DON PEDRO   (WHISPERING)   You have nothing to fear.

THE KING HAS WATCHED EVERY MOVE. BUT THE DWARF BREAKS THE TENSION AS HE STARTS DANCING WITH SUCH JOY THAT ALL THE CHILDREN CHEER. HE DANCES ROUND AND ROUND - FULL OF LOVE AND LAUGHTER. HE DANCES FASTER AND FASTER WITHOUT STOP. THE INFANTA IS ENTHRALLED AND THROWS HIM A FLOWER, AT THE END OF HIS DANCE, AS ALL THE GUESTS CRY OUT WITH APPROVAL AND APPLAUSE.

INFANTA   I love you -- I love you!! You must dance again and again.

KING   He is tired. He danced with all his heart.

INFANTA   Oh please, papa, just for a little.

KING   It is enough. Time for all the children to have a siesta. And after that he will dance again.

DWARF   Oh yes, my King.

KING   Now, go with the others and rest. You have earned it.

DWARF TUMBLES OFF-STAGE, AS HE CALLS OUT.

DWARF   Thank you, thank you, my King. My Infanta.

KING   Children, let the Duchess of Aragon lead you to your rooms.

INFANTA   Oh Father, not just yet.

KING   There will be more later.

INFANTA   But I don't want to go.

SHE BECOMES PETULANT. THE KING LOOKS HELPLESS. THE DUCHESS TACTFULLY INTERVENES.

DUCHESS   Infanta Maria, will you help me escort your guests?

THE INFANTA LOOKS TO THE KING, WHO STANDS WITHDRAWN. HE BECKONS TO THE GRAND INQUISITOR WHO FOLLOWS THE INFANTA AS SHE LEAVES WITH THE DUCHESS AND CHILDREN. THE MUSIC ACCOMPANIES THEIR EXIT AS THE REMAINDER OF THE COURT LEAVES. DON PEDRO ALONE REMAINS WITH THE KING.

KING   Your visit to Madrid is official?

DON PEDRO   It is always official to visit the Royal Palace. But there is pleasure as well in seeing the Infanta.

KING   We have not spoken these many years. But you know what I feel. How strange that my own brother, whom I loved as a boy, should be my greatest enemy. Strange, that one Mother could bear two sons so unlike each other. (SUDDEN AND DIS-ARMING) Why did you come?

DON PEDRO   To kill the Infanta! To kill the King! To kill Spain! That is what you would have me say.

KING   You never take action without some evil plot. Did you not invite me to Aragon in order to kill me? You yearn for the crown?

DON PEDRO   I care only that a Spaniard wears the crown of Spain and carries her glory into the world. A king who abandons Spain should not remain King. You talk of your love of me as a boy. It was you who read me the stories of history, with such passion and filled me with a love of country I have never forgotten. It was you who gave me the heart of Spain and I have held it ever since. What happened to that Ferdinand?

KING   He grew up and saw the world, beyond the bounds of Spain. But there in Aragon a black veil covered that vast world making it a grave. The Queen of Spain was murdered and the King died!

DON PEDRO   I asked you to Aragon so that we might talk. But we never spoke a word. I did not kill the Queen. You did! Just as you are killing Spain.

KING   By what poison did I kill the Queen? How did I harm you? How did I ever harm Spain? Because I loved?

DON PEDRO   Because you loved only for yourself.

KING   And how will you save Spain from such a terrible King?

DON PEDRO   The Infanta has come of age.

KING   If you harm her, I will kill you.

DON PEDRO   She will make a great Queen.

KING   When the time comes. She is still only a child.

DON PEDRO   She is ready now!

KING   For you - to take under your wing so that you may play king.

DON PEDRO   You have lived in your own world too long, and cannot see who she is.

KING   She is my child!

DON PEDRO   No, she is not yours. She belongs to Spain and you belong to the dead Queen.

KING   And what would you have me do?

DON PEDRO   Let Spain live! Finish your days peacefully at the Monastery in Granada. Let the Infanta become Queen. I will protect her.

KING   I have lived only to protect her from you! And you ask that I give her to you?

DON PEDRO   No -- not to me or for me. But for Spain.

KING   And am I to believe that you will not harm my child?

DON PEDRO   I swear my allegiance to the Infanta Maria.

KING   You hate me that much.

DON PEDRO   I do not hate you, that much. But I love Spain more.

> HE EXITS. THE DWARF ENTERS AND IS STARTLED AT SEEING THE KING. HE HOLDS THE INFANTA'S FLOWER LOVINGLY.

DWARF   Forgive me, my King, I thought I would be alone.

KING   You are not alone. You should save your strength little one, and rest. The children will return soon enough.

DWARF   I cannot sleep. My feet will not rest -- they wish to dance "thank you", because the Infanta loved me.

KING   Take care. Some say it is a sin to feel love in Spain.

DWARF   How could it be a sin, my Lord?

KING   I don't know. I have never found the answer.

THE KING EXITS AS THE DWARF STANDS ALONE.

DWARF   He doesn't know -- but I do. The Infanta loves me.

SONG: SHE LOVES ME

She loves me
Her lips told me so
She loves me
Her hands told me so
She loves me
That's all I want to know
She loves me.

Because --
She loves me
Her voice told me so
She loves me
Her laugh told me so
She loves me
That's all I need to know
She loves me.

I could dance all day
If she would let me stay
Just to make her smile
I would clown the while

Because --
She loves me
And what told me so?
She loves me
Well, I ought to know
She loves me
Yes, she's told me so!
She loves me, loves me, loves me!

HE DANCES ROUND AND ROUND AS HE SINGS. HE CONTINUES TO DANCE IN ECSTASY. SUDDENLY HE SEES A FIGURE IN THE MIRROR. LOOKS QUICKLY, THEN TURNS AWAY. HE PIVOTS ROUND VERY SLOWLY AND LOOKS AGAIN A LITTLE SLOWER -- TAKING A LONGER LOOK. HE TURNS AWAY ABRUPTLY. HE TAKES A LOOK AGAIN. EACH TIME HE LOOKS A LITTLE LONG-ER. HE FINALLY LOOKS FULLY IN THE MIRROR. HE DOES NOT REALISE THAT HE IS SEEING HIMSELF.

DWARF Go away! Where did you come from? I never saw you enter. Go away -- this is the Palace of the King. You are too ugly to be seen -- Go!

(HE TRIES TO MOVE HIM AWAY)

I'll call for the Guard!

(HE STRIKES THE FIGURE)

You don't belong in Madrid at the Palace. But you have -- the -- same -- shirt -- as -- mine -- the same trousers -- shoes! Who are you? Are -- you -- the -- Devil? Are -- you -- me? You -- are -- me! So ugly, so ugly -- me. How could an Infanta love me? So ugly a thing. She couldn't love me. She couldn't. She never loved me. I cannot look at you! Ugly, ugly creature. How could you come to the Palace of the Infanta and be loved by her?

(HE BEATS THE FIGURE IN THE MIRROR. THEN STARTS DANCING SLOWLY INTO MADNESS. MORE AND MORE FRENZIED - THE MUSIC OF "SHE LOVES ME". HE CALLS OUT)

She laughed at me. She -- laughed -- at -- me. Oh -- oh -- oh my heart hurts -- near to breaking. Where are the pieces? I must find -- the - pieces -- to -- my -- broken heart. The pieces --

HE COLLAPSES ONTO THE FLOOR, WRITHING IN PAIN AS THE COURT RE-ENTERS.

THE INFANTA IS BETWEEN THE GRAND INQUISITOR AND THE DUCHESS. DON PEDRO RUSHES FORWARD TO THE DWARF.

DON PEDRO What is it with you?

DWARF I am dying.

DON PEDRO Dying? From what? A moment ago you danced with life.

DWARF My heart -- the pieces -- broken. (HE DIES)

INFANTA What has happened to my birthday present, Don Pedro?

DON PEDRO He has died -- of a broken heart.

INFANTA Then bring me a dwarf that has no heart!

UPON THESE WORDS THE KING HAS ENTERED. HE SEES THE HEARTLESS INFANTA FOR THE FIRST TIME. HE TURNS TO HIS BROTHER.

KING Don Pedro, you have won. The Infanta belongs to Spain.

DON PEDRO I shall always protect her. You have my word.

THE KING GOES TO THE DWARF AND LIFTS HIM UP, CARRYING HIS BODY HIGH. NO ONE MOVES. THEY ONLY WATCH THE KING.

INFANTA   (RUNNING TO THE KING) Papa, where are you going?

KING   To the monastery in Granada.

INFANTA   Will you come back?

KING   From time to time. But you may always come to me.

HE EXITS CARRYING THE BODY OF THE DWARF.

INFANTA   (RUSHING TO THE DUCHESS AND GRAND INQUISITOR. THEY HOLD ON TO HER TO GIVE HER STRENGTH BUT SHE IS UNAFRAID) If Papa has gone, then I am Queen. Is that not so, Grand Inquisitor.

INQUISITOR   That is so. You will be Queen of Spain.

INFANTA   I am Spain. Now Don Pedro, bring me my Dwarf, that has no heart!

SHE STANDS AS SHE SAYS THIS, A LITTLE GIRL, A DWARF OF A QUEEN. EVERYONE INCLUDING DON PEDRO TURNS AND LOOKS AT THE INFANTA AS SHE SPEAKS THOSE WORDS: "A DWARF THAT HAS NO HEART." IT'S THE INFANTA -- IT IS SPAIN. THE MUSIC OF GLORIOUS SPAIN IS HEARD AS THE INFANTA REPEATS HER COMMAND TO DON PEDRO. HE EXITS TO DO HER BIDDING -- THE COURT STANDS AT ATTENTION TO THE QUEEN AS THE CURTAIN FALLS.

END OF PLAY

Red velvet

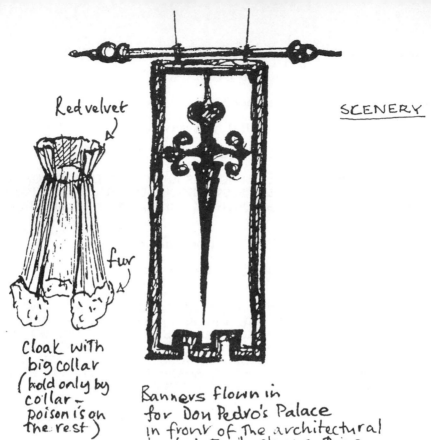

fur

Cloak with
big collar
(hold only by
collar —
poison is on
the rest)

Banners flown in
for Don Pedro's Palace
in front of The architectural
backcloth to change the scene

Drops of flowers
hung onto pillars
for The infanta's birthday

SCENERY

A painted
back-cloth
or 3D flats
if the budget
allows

throne for
King Ferdinand

COSTUMES

The Grand Inquisitor

Queen Maria

King Ferdinand
of Spain

COSTUMES

Infanta maria

The Dwarf

Don Pedro
Prince
of
Aragon

Duchess Isabel of Aragon

the legend of Scarface and Bluewater

by Blanche Marvin

THE LEGEND OF SCARFACE AND BLUE WATER

Cast:

Ke-a-taw	The oldest and wisest squaw of the village.
Singing Wind	A young unwed squaw who always complains.
Flowering Cactus	Another young squaw, plump and good natured.
Little Echo	Youngest of the squaws, sweet and lively.
Dancing Bear	The bravest warrior of the village and most arrogant.
Grey Hawk	A fine young warrior and hunter, friendly to Dancing Bear.
Laughing Face	The youngest of the warriors and hunters, not yet skilled.
Red Cloud	A wise Chief who is close to his people. Once a great warrior and hunter but wished to lead his people. He loves his only child Blue Water.
Blue Water	Daughter of Red Cloud. A young squaw, as beautiful within as without. She has great serenity and dignity, and obeys the laws of the Gods.
Scarface	A young farmer of the Kiowa tribe who has lived alone since childhood in the Sand Hills. He has an ugly scar cut across his cheek. Though poor he is proud.
Wolf	A not-so-smart animal, always hungry.
Bear	A silly fool who is vain.
Badger	A business-like, to-the-point creature.
Swan	A knowing bird.
Morning Star	An over-proud young God who loves to hunt.
Moon-Mother	A serene mother-goddess who loves her star children. She should be tall and dignified.
Sun God	The almighty God, of life and death - the Great Hunter and Healer.

Squaws, Braves of all ages and sizes in the village.
Stars and Trees of all sizes.
Three Black Birds.

Act 1	A pathway from the cornfields to the village. The village of the Shawnees. The same, a week later.
Act 2	A forest outside the village. The Sky Home of the Sun God. The Forest of the Sun God. The Sky Home of the Sun God.
Act 3	The village of the Shawnees.
Time:	An ancient legend of the Indians of the Plains who were the Great Hunters and Warriors. This story was told long before the White Man ever appeared.

THE LEGEND OF SCARFACE AND BLUE WATER

This is a play separated from the others because its intention is different. It should preferably be performed by children in schools - and by as many as you may wish. The research is to be done by the children in order to produce their own costumes, scenery, props and make-up. Co-ordinating classroom studies in social sciences, mathematics, literature, English, music, art and dance on the theme of this North American Indian legend, is highly recommended. It has been done many times very successfully and interest in the class-work has been immensely stimulated. There is no set style, only place and period. Music, movement, costume, scenery, props are selected to suit the American Indian culture and by what the children prefer and can accomplish. Drums were used. The response to rhythm is universal. What child does not enjoy playing Cowboys and Indians? Age range can be in primary schools up to 14 years of age.

Scarface and Blue Water was written and produced as an end of term project for St Paul's Way School, ILEA. The entire school term was devoted to the theme of the American Indian or tribal life of man.

There is so much basic familiarity in the theme of Indians that every child responded immediately with a sense of pleasure. Taking this emotional contact as my point of reference I then could add all the information and background about Indians without being pedantic.

Every detail in the play is accurate - every custom and attitude. The essence of the fantasy where the animals become characters on an equal level with humans is part of the Indian culture. They knew and understood nature and tried to maintain a balance that we in our current civilisation have long forgotten and denied. The mores and ethics - the wisdoms - the knowledge of natural forces - farming - weaving - tanning were profound and varied with the tribes and their habitats. Not all Indians were nomadic people. Some lived in tents but others in cliffs. From the cliche concepts we explore other avenues and learn more about man than was ever expected. All the interconnecting links were important to the production. So the integration of studies culminating in a play brought about a natural motivation to learn and knowledge became enjoyable as well as useful. Each contribution from each child brought something special on its own. Concerted learning gave impetus to an understanding of tribal living.

It was interesting to hear comments from the children. The Indians they felt bore no relationship to themselves. But when discussions began as to how to play the parts, each character became real as they understood the mechanism of the people and their relationship to society. And that is what theatre is all about. The younger generation's interest in pop music and dance rhythms is close to tribal interpretations - the beads, belts, bells, long hair, clothes - are all indicative of tribal existence.

Here through a single production we achieved a Renaissance approach to learning and living. It became a total experience. With the help and enthusiasm of each teacher coordinating in his lessons the points of view relative to the production and checking with one another, the director, Michael Boakes, then pulled together all the reins and created a play which belonged to everyone and not just the Drama Department. A performance at the Place Theatre gave an added reward to the children's efforts and four more performances were requested by other schools who attended.

For those who are interested in this play as a work on its own, the play is here. The characterisations should not be imposed, but let the personality of each child come through in each part. Do not be tricked into mouthing words but let the children be allowed their own rhythms of speech. Accents are not important. Each character in the play is particularised and can easily be cast accordingly.

The love story is short and shy so that the children will not be embarrassed by it. The taunting of the braves over the love is quite natural. The Sun God should be an adult voice off-stage or on tape.

It must not be of concern how well the parts are played but how much each child has received from the production. If the children enjoy themselves so will the audience. The scenery and costumes were part of the children's work, as were the wigwam, the open fire and props.

We had slides made from the original drawings. The stars and forest were played by the children and in a dance pattern made their entrances and exits. It was one of the highlights of the production.

ACT ONE

IN FRONT OF THE CURTAIN, KE-A-TAW, THE OLDEST SQUAW
OF THE VILLAGE ENTERS RIGHT. SHE IS CARRYING A HEAVY
BASKET FILLED WITH CORN. FROM THE BASKET HANG MOCC-
ASINS AS WELL.

KE-A-TAW Flowering Cactus, Singing Wind - make haste! (NO
ANSWER) Singing Wind - Flowering Cactus - Little Echo! Can it
be that such an old squaw as I moves faster than the young
squaws?

OTHER SQUAWS ENTER CARRYING THEIR BASKETS WITH CORN,
ON THEIR HEADS. SINGING WIND IS VERY THIN AND FLOWER-
ING CACTUS SHOULD BE FAT. THEY ARGUE AS THEY ENTER.

SINGING WIND Carrying all this corn in one basket! We could
carry less at a time.

FLOWERING CACTUS Complain, complain, all day long. Let's
change baskets. (SHE OFFERS TO CHANGE BASKETS)

SINGING WIND Yours is probably heavier.

FLOWERING CACTUS What would happen to you if you had nothing
to complain about?

KE-A-TAW Instead of thanking the Rain God for our great
harvest, I hear words which only offend him. If you had no
corn to feed your children, if the fields lay barren, and the
plain without deer or buffalo and -- (ALL SQUAWS JOIN IN AND
ALL FINISH THE PHRASE WITH HER AS THEY NOW KNOW IT BY HEART)
-- you had only roots to feed upon, as we did many moons ago,
you would know what it means to have the Rain God be Angry.

SQUAWS PAUSE TO REST, SOME USE THEIR BASKETS TO SIT
ON, SOME RUB THEIR BACKS, OTHERS THEIR NECKS AND
SHOULDERS. IT IS HOT AND THE SUN IS STRONG. LITTLE
ECHO JOINS THEM.

LITTLE ECHO Blue Water won't come from the fields, Ke-a-Taw.
She's still drying and tying the corn.

SINGING WIND Her goodness makes me tired and lately it's even
worse. Tomorrow is another day. Let her tie and dry the corn
then.

KE-A-TAW Little Echo - go bring Blue Water back. Today is
the day of the Great Hunt.

LITTLE ECHO Blue Water knows. She said she would come back
as soon as she was finished. I'll help you carry your basket,
Singing Wind. (MOVES TO TAKE BASKET)

SINGING WIND   You'd probably drop it. And then I would have to spend more time picking corn up from the ground.

FLOWERING CACTUS   Wait until we start to grind the corn into flour. You'll have plenty of time then - just to sit and complain.

KE-A-TAW   I'm sure Blue Water is thanking the Rain God even at this moment for the harvest.

SINGING WIND   If she prayed less and played more, our Chief's daughter would be married.

LITTLE ECHO   There is not a Brave in our village who would not marry Blue Water. (PUTS SINGING WIND'S BASKET ON HER HEAD)

FLOWERING CACTUS   Then why doesn't she marry?

KE-A-TAW   Oh, let us hasten home. Gossip can wait for the evening sun when the hunters have gone.

SQUAWS CONTINUE CROSSING TO STAGE LEFT.

LITTLE ECHO   If Chief Red Cloud's son had only lived - it wouldn't matter when or who Blue Water married.

KE-A-TAW   If! If! If the Sun God took vengeance he could turn the land into a ball of fire. If I were not old - I would be young.

LITTLE ECHO   Excuse my dreaming, Ke-a-Taw. (PUTS DOWN BASKET) I'm beginning to feel the weight.

SINGING WIND   Ah, but if the basket were empty, it would be light.

KE-A-TAW   (SARCASTICALLY) And if it were empty, we would not have food for the winter. Home at last.

ALL EXIT STAGE LEFT. CURTAIN.

SCENE TWO

CURTAINS OPEN ON AN INDIAN VILLAGE ON THE PLAINS. A BACKDROP, OR CURTAIN HUNG FROM STAGE RIGHT TO LEFT COVERING THE UPSTAGE AREA, IS PAINTED WITH A SKY, SUN AND CLOUDS. THE DISTANT HILLS CAN ALSO BE PAINTED BUT IN MUTED COLOURS. STAR MOBILES, HANG DOWN BY STRONG THREAD FROM THE CEILING OF THE STAGE IN THE DISTANCE.

UPSTAGE CENTRE IS CHIEF RED CLOUD'S TENT PAINTED WITH INDIAN SYMBOLS. ANOTHER WAY TO DECORATE THE TENT IS BY COLOURING VARIOUS SHAPES OF MACARONI AND GLUEING THEM TO THE CLOTH OR PAPER USED ON THE OUTSIDE OF THE TENT. THREE OR FIVE BROOMSTICKS CAN BE THE FRAME

FOR THE TENT, TIED TOGETHER WITH WIRE AT THE TOP. THE
BASES OF THE STICKS CAN BE PUT INTO PAILS OF SAND OR
DIRT. STAGE RIGHT IS A FIRE MADE OF STICKS WITH RED
JELLS PROJECTING FROM THE TOP, GIVING THE EFFECT OF
A BURNING FIRE. STAGE LEFT HAS A HUGE FLAT PAPIER
MACHE STONE ALMOST RESEMBLING A TABLE TOP. IT IS THE
GRINDING STONE USED BY THE VILLAGE TO GRIND OR POUND
THE CORN INTO FLOUR. A STRONG, THICK PIECE OF WOOD
PAINTED GREY WITH SHADINGS OF BLACK WOULD ALSO MAKE
A FINE GRINDING STONE.

WOMEN ENTER STAGE LEFT TO FIND THE BRAVES NEAR THE
FIRE. BOWS AND ARROWS ARE SCATTERED BY THE FIRE. THE
BRAVES ARE ALL INVOLVED IN THE FIGHT GOING ON BETWEEN
DANCING BEAR AND GREY HAWK, AND ADLIB ADVICE TO BOTH.
THE EXCITEMENT IS HIGH. THE TWO ARE FIGHTING WITH ARMS
TIED BEHIND THEIR BACKS. DANCING BEAR IS OLDER AND
STRONGER. GREY HAWK IS QUICKER AND MORE ARROGANT.

BRAVE 1   Use the left shoulder. One quick move and you can
win Blue Water's hand.

BRAVE 2   Use your right shoulder. Push hard - harder. Blue
Water's yours.

ALL   You missed.

ALL MOAN AS GREY HAWK FALLS. WOMEN ARE DISGUSTED.
THEY CARRY THEIR BASKETS TO THE GRINDING STONE. GREY
HAWK GETS TO HIS FEET AND THE FIGHT RESUMES.

KE-A-TAW   (STOPS NEAR CIRCLE OF BRAVES) Is this how our
bravest warriors prepare for the hunt? Shame!

BRAVE 3   Kick him!

BRAVE 4   Trip him!

BOTH BRAVES FALL AND THE SHOUTS ARE ENORMOUS: "Get
up!", "Hold him down" etc.

KE-A-TAW   This is the sound of Coyotes not Braves. Stop!!

NO ONE LISTENS.

SINGING WIND   It's a fine game.

CHIEF RED CLOUD ENTERS STAGE LEFT WITH THE ELDERS.
HE WEARS FULL INDIAN HEAD-DRESS. DANCING BEAR, GREY
HAWK STOP THE FIGHTING AT ONCE. SUDDENLY ALL IS QUIET.

RED CLOUD   My two greatest warriors fight each other, while
their Chief is away at the storehouse. Is this how you protect
the village?

GREY HAWK   (GASPING FOR BREATH) I am fighting for the hand of Blue Water.

DANCING BEAR   (BITTER) I too am fighting for her hand. It should be mine. I am the eldest Brave and the greatest hunter.

GREY HAWK   But Blue Water prefers me.

RED CLOUD   This is not the time or place to decide such serious matters. After the Hunt we will discuss the marriage of Blue Water.

BLUE WATER   (JUST ENTERING STAGE LEFT) My father did I hear you speak of my marriage - and before all the village?

RED CLOUD   It must one day happen, my daughter. But we will wait till after the Hunt.

DANCING BEAR   I won't go to the Hunt without an answer from Blue Water.

GREY HAWK   (CHALLENGED) Nor will I.

ALL BRAVES   (SHOUTING) Blue Water, choose your Brave! Choose your Brave! Choose your Brave!

RED CLOUD   Chief Red Cloud has spoken. We will wait till after the Hunt.

DANCING BEAR   I ask for Blue Water's hand and each time I am told to wait.

KE-A-TAW   I've already made the moccasins for your wedding, Blue Water. Choose a husband.

SINGING WIND   Look at the great warriors who want to marry you.

ALL THE VILLAGE NOW JOIN IN AND SHOUT 'Choose your Brave, Choose your Brave, Choose your Brave!' THE BRAVES BEGIN TO FORM A CIRCLE AND DANCE ROUND BLUE WATER WHO STANDS STILL WITH HEAD BOWED THROUGHOUT THE DANCE.

RED CLOUD   There is no choice now. We cannot wait till after the Hunt. The Braves have begun the Wedding Dance.

THE DANCING OF THE BRAVES IS FIERCE, SHOWING THEIR BRAVERY. THE PASSIONS OF THE VILLAGE ARE AROUSED. THE WOMEN CLAP HANDS AND STAMP THEIR FEET, AND SHOUT IN RHYTHM, AS CHIEF RED CLOUD AND THE ELDERS SIT IN FRONT OF THE TENT AND WATCH. WHEN THE DANCE IS FINISHED, ALL WAIT FOR CHIEF RED CLOUD TO SPEAK. HE RISES AND THE WHOLE VILLAGE IS STILL.

RED CLOUD   The warriors have all danced the Wedding Dance of the bull-foxes. Now according to the laws of our Fathers, I may no longer choose Blue Water's husband. But Blue Water herself must choose. She may give her hand to any Brave she wishes.

MURMERS OF GREAT EXCITEMENT PASS AMONG THE VILLAGE.

BRAVES   Blue Water must choose!

RED CLOUD   Dancing Bear, Grey Hawk, stand with the other Braves.

WOMEN   Which Brave will it be?

RED CLOUD   Daughter, choose your warrior, and remember that your choice will be the next chief when I am gone.

BLUE WATER   I beg of you my Father, I cannot choose.

DEAD SILENCE.

RED CLOUD   (ANGRY)   Will the daughter of Chief Red Cloud disobey her father before the whole village? You choose now or go to the Sand Hills and there wander the plains!

BLUE WATER   Please my father, do not punish me. I wish that I could choose a husband like the other squaws. But I must obey a law stronger than one of my father.

RED CLOUD   (ANGRY)   Who is stronger than Chief Red Cloud?

BLUE WATER   The Sun God himself.

RED CLOUD   And he tells you to disobey your father?

BLUE WATER   Two moons ago I gave him my promise never to wed a Brave from our village, but only one from outside our tribe, and this Brave must find the consent of the Sun God himself. In return he granted long life and a land of plenty to our people.

DANCING BEAR AND GREY HAWK MOVE AWAY. THERE IS DEEP DISAPPOINTMENT IN THE VILLAGE AT THIS NEWS.

RED CLOUD   And what if you broke this promise?

BLUE WATER   If I disobeyed, the Sun God would destroy us.

RED CLOUD   (RESIGNED)   Then the Ruler of the Skies is the Ruler on Earth. (TO WHOLE VILLAGE) And we must all listen.

KE-A-TAW   Blue Water is giving us her life. The Gods know this and we give thanks.

ALL WOMEN KNEEL.

LITTLE ECHO   Then there won't be a wedding?

RED CLOUD   My daughter, you have blessed your people by your sacrifice. Go brave warriors -- go to the Hunt. And let the Wedding Dance of the bull-foxes henceforth be known as the Sun Dance. Named for the Great Father of the Hunt, the Sun God, who gives us the deer and the buffalo. Go and return home rich, with the rewards of the plains.

> THE BRAVES GATHER THEIR BOWS & ARROWS AND MARCH OUT STAGE LEFT. THE WOMEN WAVE GOODBYE AND START TAKING THE CORN FROM THEIR BASKETS AS RED CLOUD AND THE ELDERS SURROUND BLUE WATER, CENTRE STAGE.

RED CLOUD   (CALLS AFTER BRAVES) Go young hunters - go to the Hunt and return home rich, with the rewards of the plains.

CURTAIN

SCENE THREE

> A WEEK LATER. SCENE IS THE SAME. ONLY THE FIRE STICKS STAGE RIGHT ARE GONE. THE BRAVES HAVE RETURNED FROM THE HUNT AND ARE GATHERED IN A SEMI-CIRCLE SPRAWLED OUT ON THE GROUND. THEY ARE GAMBLING ON A STICK GAME. TWO STICKS HAVE THREE OR FOUR NOTCHES CARVED ON THEM ON SEVERAL SIDES. THEY THROW THE STICKS AND GUESS THE NUMBERS. A GAME SIMILAR TO DICE. THEY ADD THE NUMBER OF NOTCHES ON WHATEVER SIDE THE STICKS FALL. THE BRAVES BET THEIR BOWS AND ARROWS, THEIR BELTS AND JEWELRY. ONE BRAVE HAS EVEN LOST HIS MOCCASINS. THEY ARE ALL EXCITED, SHOUTING WITH ANGER AT TIMES.

DANCING BEAR   The Fire God is on my side. (HE HAS JUST WON A BOW) I bet seven.

GREY HAWK   Then I'll take the Water God and (MENACINGLY) put out your fire. I bet eight.

BRAVE 3   Grey Hawk, my moccasins won't fit you. Let me try to win them back.

GREY HAWK   No.

BRAVE 3   Then I'll bet ten for my ten toes.

BRAVE 4   Why not two for your two front teeth? Or none for that empty head.

BRAVE 3   I'll shoot you! Where's my bow and arrow?

BRAVE 4   You lost it games and games ago, idiot. I bet five. Now throw the sticks.

DANCING BEAR   (THROWS STICKS) Number nine is the number.

BRAVE 5   I thought it would be and I didn't bet. (HITS THE GROUND IN ANGER)

BRAVE 3   To lose by one notch! I was the closest to nine. Can't I win?

DANCING BEAR   Why do you always want to change the rules? No! You didn't win! Let's bet.

> THE NUMBER CALLING CONTINUES AS A YOUNG INDIAN MAN ENTERS STAGE LEFT. HE HAS A DEEP SCAR ACROSS HIS CHEEK. HIS FEET ARE BARE AND HIS CLOTHES IN RAGS. HE IS OBVIOUSLY VERY POOR, AND CARRIES A FEW EARS OF CORN.

SCARFACE   I've come for a pair of moccasins in exchange for the corn. Where may I find the old squaw Ke-A-Taw?

DANCING BEAR   How do you know Ke-A-Taw?

SCARFACE   Who has not heard of Ke-A-Taw and her famous moccasins?

GREY HAWK   How long have you walked without moccasins?

SCARFACE   A long time.

DANCING BEAR   Where is your bow and arrow?

SCARFACE   I have neither.

GREY HAWK   Doesn't your father or Chief have one?

SCARFACE   There is no Chief. I have neither mother nor father. I live alone in the Sand Hills.

BRAVE 1   Who cut your cheek?

BRAVE 2   What's your name? Ugly Bear?

> THEY ALL LAUGH.

SCARFACE   I bear this scar across my cheek from the wars made upon my village. All my people, the Kiowa, were killed except for me. My name is Scarface. Now tell me where the Old Mother lives.

BRAVE 3   You're standing by her tent. Just there.

SCARFACE   That is the tent of a Chief.

BRAVE 4   You may be ugly but you can see.

BRAVE 2   It is the tent of our Chief.

BRAVE 1   The Chief's daughter, Blue Water lives there too. The most beautiful squaw west of the sun.

> KE-A-TAW COMES IN FROM STAGE RIGHT, CARRYING A PAIR OF MOCCASINS ON A STICK. SHE LOOKS UP AND SEES ALL THE YOUNG INDIANS. SHE ALSO SEES THE GAMBLING STICKS, AND BECOMES ANGERED.

KE-A-TAW   Gambling? The young warriors and hunters are busy with the sticks. Why don't you sharpen your arrows and make new bows? Why don't you stretch the hides of the deer and buffalo so that the women may tan and sew them? The Great Spirit sees what you do. He knows. No wonder He forbade Blue Water to marry one of you.

DANCING BEAR   Didn't we return from the Hunt with plenty of game?

GREY HAWK   Haven't we brought enough food and skins to store for many winters?

BRAVE 4   Yes. We should be rewarded, not punished.

BRAVE 3   Even the Gods gamble.

KE-A-TAW   Only Blue Water protects you.

SCARFACE   Old Mother, I am Scarface from the Sand Hills. I come to beg a pair of moccasins from you in exchange for the only food I can grow - these few ears of corn.

KE-A-TAW   And what will you do with the moccasins if I give them to you?

BRAVE 1   He'll ask for Blue Water's hand in marriage.

BRAVE 2   Yes - here is a Brave just right for the Sun God. Give him the moccasins.

BRAVE 3   Let him ask Blue Water without the moccasins.

BRAVE 4   Here's the tent of Blue Water.

BRAVE 1   The only weapon you need is your tongue. Ask her hand in marriage. Let's see how brave you are!

> THEY ALL LAUGH.

SCARFACE   I'm not afraid but I know nothing of the Chief's daughter.

KE-A-TAW   (TO BRAVES) Boastful hunters! Blue Water protects you and you make fun of her. Beware! (TO SCARFACE) I'll give you the moccasins, Scarface, and you may keep your corn for we have plenty. Ask Blue Water for her hand in marriage. The

Sun God may look more kindly upon someone like you.

SCARFACE   Ke-A-Taw, Old Mother of many sons, I have neither bow nor arrow, nor father to teach me the skill of the Hunter. But my heart is brave.

KE-A-TAW   Then go to Blue Water. She prays for a miracle.

SCARFACE   I will ask for the hand of Blue Water, not as a game these warriors play but because she prays. I am not afraid.

> SHE GIVES HIM THE MOCCASINS AND EXITS STAGE LEFT. THE BRAVES MOVE STAGE LEFT WATCHING SCARFACE CAREFULLY, AND READY TO LAUGH AT THEIR JOKE. SCARFACE GOES UP TO THE CHIEF'S TENT.

SCARFACE   (SHOUTS) I am Scarface from the Sand Hills and I come to speak with the Chief's daughter, Blue Water. I ask that we may talk face to face.

BLUE WATER   (FROM THE TENT) I am Blue Water, daughter of Chief Red Cloud and will speak with Scarface of the Sand Hills. What is your message?

SCARFACE   I am not like the young hunters of your village, but I am brave. I... I...

> HE CANNOT SPEAK ANY MORE AS BLUE WATER COMES OUT OF THE TENT. HE SEES HER FOR THE FIRST TIME AND IS OVER-WHELMED WITH HER BEAUTY. THE OTHER BRAVES NOD AS IF TO SAY "I told you so."

BLUE WATER   Your words were as quick as lightning before and now your tongue is as still as the windless summer. Speak again young Brave. I will listen. I hear even the silence.

SCARFACE   I am a poor planter who must plough his corn into barren soil. My people are no more. I came to ask Blue Water's hand because I was challenged. Now I ask the hand of Blue Water, who stands as alone as I, in this land of plenty, because I love her.

BLUE WATER   Your words run as deep as the river. You see the shadows in my heart. (SHE LOOKS AT THE SCAR ON HIS CHEEK AND TOUCHES IT) I feel what you are feeling, and see the scar on your cheek. Yes. (PAUSE) I would marry you, Scarface. The Braves of my village are forbidden to me. No other could I choose, but only a stranger such as you. Now we must wait for a sign from the Sun God since I cannot wed without His consent. (SPACE THIS SPEECH OUT WITH PAUSES. DO NOT RUSH)

SCARFACE   (STRONGLY) I will not wait for the sign, but I will go to the Sun God and seek his consent. To find an answer for you without question, I would journey farther than the sky.

ACT TWO

BLUE WATER We must set the sign. If the Sun God consents, he will heal the scar on your cheek.

SCARFACE Where will I find him, Blue Water? Which is the way to go?

BLUE WATER You must go to the West where his bed lies. Far over the hills to the edge of the sky.

SCARFACE Then I will find the home of the Sun God and we will wed in His Dawn.

> SCARFACE SLOWLY EXITS TO STAGE RIGHT AS BLUE WATER BIDS FAREWELL. THE NOW QUIET BRAVES, WITH SERIOUS FACES, WATCH HIM GO. IF POSSIBLE, THE LIGHTS SHOULD SLOWLY FADE OUT ON SCARFACE AND ON BLUE WATER.
>
> END OF ACT ONE.

SCENE ONE

> THE BACKDROP OF ACT ONE AND THE STAR MOBILES REMAIN; THE OTHER SET PIECES ARE CLEARED AWAY. A LENGTH OF BLUE TAFFETA, NO LONGER THAN THE PROSCENIUM DIMEN-SIONS, IS ON THE FLOOR IN FRONT OF THE BACK-DROP. CHILDREN REPRESENTING TREES ARRANGE THEMSELVES ALL OVER THE STAGE. TREE COSTUMES CAN BE MADE OF CARD-BOARD AND POSTER PAINT. THE TOPS OF THE TREES SHOULD EXTEND OVER THE HEADS OF THE CHILDREN, AS THEY ARE THE LEAVES. A BEAUTIFUL WARRIOR'S JACKET, BOWS AND ARROWS PAINTED SILVER, AND A DECORATED PAIR OF MOCC-ASINS WITH COLOURED FEATHERS ARE HIDDEN BEHIND TWO OF THE TREES, FOR USE LATER IN THE PLAY.
>
> SCARFACE ENTERS STAGE RIGHT. HE WANDERS BETWEEN SEVERAL TREES, LOOKING FOR THE PATH TO THE SUN GOD. HE HAS BEEN WALKING FOR A LONG TIME AND IS VERY TIRED.

SCARFACE I've walked west – through the forest – further than I've ever been – but still no path to the Sun God. I'm so tired. I can't go on much longer. (HE SITS DOWN) I must rest for a little while.

> HE FALLS ASLEEP DESPITE HIMSELF. AS HE SLEEPS, THE WOLF COMES FROM STAGE LEFT ON ALL FOURS. HE WALKS WITH A LIMP. HE IS HUNGRY. HE SNIFFS AROUND AND QUIETLY STALKS SCARFACE.

WOLF Gr... gr... I see, I shall have a belly full for the winter. (HE IS VERY CLOSE TO SCARFACE)

SCARFACE (OPENS EYES SLOWLY BUT DOES NOT MOVE AS WOLF FREEZES) Why, you must be Sharp-Tooth, the wolf whose broken paw I mended. Old Friend, don't you know me?

WOLF (LOOKS SHARPLY) Scarface! From over the River? What are you doing so far from home?

SCARFACE Sharp-Tooth, maybe you can help me. I'm looking for the path to the Sun God. My life depends on finding him.

WOLF I'm not as clever as I'm supposed to be. I don't know the path to the Sun God. But my friend the Bear is friendlier than I and knows more about the forest!

SCARFACE Where can I find him?

WOLF To the north, by the purple hills.

WOLF EXITS.

SCARFACE I thank you, old friend.

SCARFACE WALKS SLOWLY IN PLACE WHILE TREES UPSTAGE RIGHT AND CENTRE PART ONE YARD TO EITHER SIDE RE-VEALING A CARDBOARD CUT-OUT OF THE PURPLE HILLS. SCARFACE TURNS AND WALKS TO THE HILLS. MUSIC CAN HELP ESTABLISH THE PASSAGE OF TIME.

SCARFACE Bear? Bear, where are you? What shall I do? (SUDDENLY AN IDEA OCCURS) Ah - (CALLS OUT) Honey cone! Honey cone! Honey cone! I have some sweet honey cone.

BEAR (GRUFF VOICE OFFSTAGE) Where is this honey cone? I have never found any.

SCARFACE There is none.

BEAR (FURIOUS) None! Then I shall feed on meat, (BEAR IS ABOUT TO ATTACK) instead of sweet.

SCARFACE Brother Bear, wait a moment. Sharp-Tooth sent me to find you.

BEAR (SUDDEN CHANGE IN HIS NATURE. PROUDLY) To find me? Sharp-Tooth sent you to me. (CHANGES AGAIN. SUSPICIOUSLY) Are you poisoned meat?

SCARFACE No. (SMILES) But he sent me to find you because you are the cleverest beast in the forest. (IMPORTANTLY) I am looking for the path to the Sun God.

BEAR (PROUDLY) That is important, but I don't know the way to the Sun God. (LONGINGLY) I wish I could find some honey.

SCARFACE You may have my corn. It will sharpen your eyes.

BEAR Will it? Then I'll take the corn. Find the striped badger. He knows the underearth and can show you its ways. I'm sure the path to the Sun God is there.

SCARFACE   Where will I find the badger?

BEAR   Follow your nose and it will lead you...

BADGER ROLLS IN FROM STAGE RIGHT IN A TIGHT BALL. HE IS VERY BRISK AND BUSINESSLIKE. BEAR, STARTLED, LUMBERS OFF STAGE LEFT.

SCARFACE   Striped Badger! Where did you come from?

BADGER   (POINTS TO THE GROUND) I live here. Now, what do you want of me?

SCARFACE   I am looking for the path to the Sun God.

BADGER   (ANNOYED) I don't know of such a path.

SCARFACE   (PLEADS) The Sun God waits for me... please help me.

BADGER   Go to the Black Glass Mountain. There at the base is a stream. Call to the White Swan - very gently - and she will tell you the way. (ROLLS OFF STAGE RIGHT)

TREES GATHER ROUND SCARFACE. THEY HIDE HIM FROM VIEW AS THEY CIRCLE AROUND HIM AND ESCORT HIM UPSTAGE LEFT. THERE THEY UNFOLD AND FORM A WIDE WEDGE-SHAPED PATH TO THE BLACK GLASS MOUNTAIN.

SCARFACE   (CALLS SOFTLY)   White Swan of the Black Glass Mountain, don't be afraid. Scarface calls out to you for help.

WHITE SWAN DESCENDS WITH WINGS OUTSTRETCHED INTO THE OPENING MADE BY THE TREES AND SETTLES ON THE BLUE TAFFETA RUNNER.

WHITE SWAN   The leaves of the forest carried your message. I heard you before you called. Hold on to me and I will take you to the Sun God.

SCENE TWO

SCARFACE HOLDS SWAN'S DOWNSTAGE WING AND THEY EXIT UPSTAGE LEFT. SOME OF THE TREES SLOWLY MOVE OFF STAGE RIGHT AND LEFT. TWO STAGEHANDS, ONE AT EITHER END OF THE BLUE RUNNER PICK IT UP AND MOVE IT DOWNSTAGE, AS SWAN AND SCARFACE RE-ENTER CENTRE LEFT, CROSS AND EXIT CENTRE STAGE RIGHT. THE REST OF THE TREES EXIT STAGE RIGHT AND LEFT.

WHEN THE LAST TREE IS GONE WE SEE THE BEAUTIFUL SHIELD MADE OF CARDBOARD RESTING DOWN CENTRE STAGE AGAINST A PAPIER MACHE ROCK. THE SHIELD IS PAINTED SILVER WITH BRIGHTLY COLOURED MACARONI JEWELS PASTED ON IT, SILVER BOWS AND ARROWS, A WAR JACKET OF SILVER, AND THE FEATHER MOCCASINS ARE ALL ON THE GROUND.

THEY WERE HIDDEN BEFORE, BEHIND TWO TREES. SCARFACE ENTERS DOWNSTAGE RIGHT, FOLLOWS THE SILK AND SEES THE BEAUTIFUL WEAPONS. HE DOES NOT TOUCH THEM BUT LOOKS FOR THEIR OWNER. AT THAT MOMENT MORNING STAR APPEARS, FROM STAGE LEFT.

THIS MUST BE A TALL BOY PAINTED WITH A MASK-LIKE FACE OR MASK, AND WEARING A STAR CROWN. THE YOUNG GOD COMES IN CAUTIOUSLY. HE HAS A BOW AND ARROW WHICH HE AIMS AT SCARFACE WHO LOOKS AT HIM, STUNNED.

SCARFACE   Don't shoot! I have come in peace! You must be the Sun God. (KNEELS)

MORNING STAR   (LAUGHS) I am Morning Star, son of the Sun God. You could not look upon the Sun God and live. His blazing light would burn you. Now who are you - and why should I not shoot?

SCARFACE   (RISING) I am Scarface of the Sand Hills. I was sent here by Blue Water, to ask the Sun God to grant me her hand in marriage.

MORNING STAR   I have heard of Blue Water. (PUTS DOWN BOW) You are a brave warrior to have come so far on such a dangerous quest.

SCARFACE   I am not a warrior, only a poor planter who would go to the ends of the earth for Blue Water.

MORNING STAR   (GATHERING HIS WEAPONS AND PUTTING ON MOCCASINS AND JACKET) I am the greatest warrior of the heavens and the earth, and still I would not make such a long journey for the hand of a squaw. Is it so important to see the Sun God that you would risk your life?

SCARFACE   I cannot wed Blue Water without his consent.

MORNING STAR   Then why marry her?

SCARFACE   Because she is my love. (PAUSE)

MORNING STAR   I will take you home with me and you shall meet my Moon-Mother. She knows more about love than I do. But you must do as she says or the Sun God will destroy you.

SCARFACE   Lead me and I will follow.

THEY EXIT UPSTAGE RIGHT.

SCENE THREE

AS SCARFACE AND MORNING STAR EXIT TWO STARS ENTER STAGE RIGHT AND GATHER IN THE BLUE TAFFETA RUNNER. MOON-MOTHER ENTERS STAGE LEFT HOLDING ONTO THE OTHER END OF THE RUNNER. STARS GENTLY DRAW MOON-

MOTHER IN A CIRCLE LEAVING HER UPSTAGE LEFT. AFTER PLACING THE RUNNER ON THE FLOOR IN FRONT OF MOON-MOTHER, STARS TAKE UP POSITIONS ONE AT EITHER END OF THE RUNNER. MOON-MOTHER HAS MASK-LIKE MAKE-UP, A LONG SILVER DRESS, A CRESCENT CROWN, AND SHE TOO MUST BE TALL. SCARFACE AND MORNING STAR, ENTER STAGE RIGHT AND CROSS TO MOON-MOTHER.

MOON-MOTHER   (FEARFUL) My son, who have you brought home? The Sun God will blaze in fury.

SCARFACE   Moon-Mother, I begged Morning Star to bring me here. I must ask the Sun God for his permission to marry Blue Water.

MOON-MOTHER   But he will destroy you if he sees you. You must go back.

SCARFACE   I would rather the Sun God destroy me than not wed Blue Water.

MOON-MOTHER   If you wish to speak to the Sun God, then you must earn the right to do so.
      (SUDDENLY THE COLOUR CHANGES TO RED)
(TERRIFIED) The Sun God is coming home. You are in terrible danger. Quickly hide under my veil. Let us pray he will not see you.

      A BRIGHT LIGHT APPEARS AND EVERYTHING ELSE ON STAGE IS DIM.

SUN GOD   (BOOMING ADULT MALE VOICE OFF STAGE) I smell a human, Mother Moon. Who are you hiding?

MOON-MOTHER   Oh my husband I ask so little of you. I travel my course alone. Please grant me the life of this human.

SUN GOD   Why should I grant a special favour to him?

MOON-MOTHER   He is a human who loves.

SUN GOD   Let me see him.

MOON-MOTHER   He would burn if I uncover him.

SUN GOD   (ANGRY) Am I not the Sun God? Is not my word, law? Let me see him.

MOON-MOTHER   Your word is law but you would burn to ash an innocent boy and take from me a child I could love.

SUN GOD   (AFTER A PAUSE) Very well, Moon Mother, you may keep him.

MOON-MOTHER   I thank you, my husband. May he become Morning Star's brother to keep him company in the heavens?

SUN GOD   So it shall be Moon-Mother, twin stars in the skies. I will go to lie down now. The earth will rest with me.

> LIGHT DISAPPEARS AND STAGE LIGHTS COME UP. SCARFACE AND MORNING STAR STAND SIDE BY SIDE NEAR MOON-MOTHER.

SCARFACE   I thank you, Moon-Mother, for saving my life. But what can I do to earn my right to speak with the Sun God?

MOON-MOTHER   Time will bring an answer. Perhaps when the stars have moved across the heavens. Till then we must wait.

MORNING STAR   Come with me Scarface, to the forest, where we shall hunt. Here, take one of my bows and some arrows.

SCARFACE   But I've never shot with a bow and arrow.

MORNING STAR   I will teach you in the forest.

MOON-MOTHER   Morning Star, remember my warning. Do not shoot the big black birds by the stream. For if you do, you will go to your death just as your brother stars did; never again to be seen in the skies.

> MOON-MOTHER EXITS STAGE LEFT AND THE TWO STARS TAKE THE BLUE TAFFETA RUNNER AND LAY IT DOWNSTAGE LEFT TO RIGHT. TREES OF SILVER CARDBOARD IN THE SHAPE OF GIANT STARS ENTER UPSTAGE RIGHT. SCARFACE AND MORNING STAR CROSS FROM STAGE LEFT TAKING SMALL STRIDES. THEY STAY SIDE BY SIDE. THEY WILL BE AIMING THEIR ARROWS AT THE TREES UPSTAGE RIGHT.

SCENE FOUR

MORNING STAR   Hold the bow firm, like so - pull back the string with the arrow - aim - release the string and let the arrow fly -

SCARFACE   What great marksmanship.

MORNING STAR   Now you.

> (HE GIVES SCARFACE A BOW AND ARROW. SCARFACE FOLLOWS INSTRUCTIONS AND SHOOTS WITH GREAT SKILL, TO MORNING STAR'S SURPRISE)

Your arrow flew with the speed of lightning. Let's see who can mark that tree - just over there. (POINTS UPSTAGE)

> WHILE THEY ARE NOTCHING THEIR ARROWS, THREE BLACK BIRDS ENTER DOWNSTAGE. MORNING STAR TURNS SLOWLY AND

SEES THE BIRDS. SCARFACE WATCHES HIM RAISE HIS BOW TO
SHOOT THE BIRDS. SCARFACE CALLS OUT.

SCARFACE   (KNOCKS BOW AWAY FROM MORNING STAR) Don't shoot,
you will die!

BIRDS LOOK UP. BEFORE MORNING STAR CAN RECOVER HIS
BOW AND ARROW, SCARFACE SHOOTS WITH PERFECT AIM. THE
BIRDS START TO FLY AT SCARFACE BUT HE SHOOTS THREE
ARROWS QUICKLY AND THE THREE BIRDS FALL. HE LOOKS AT
THE BIRDS IN SHAME, THEN TURNS AWAY.

MORNING STAR   (ARROGANTLY) They were my birds. It was my
hunt.

SCARFACE   (SCOLDS) It could have been your death, and as
night follows day, my death would follow.

MORNING STAR   My mother fears too much for me.

SCARFACE   But you are the only Morning Star.

MORNING STAR   (VERY HAPPY) We must tell Moon Mother what
has happened. The birds are dead.

TREES QUIETLY EXIT UPSTAGE RIGHT. MORNING STAR AND
SCARFACE CARRY THE BIRDS OFF DOWNSTAGE RIGHT THEN
RE-ENTER AND CROSS TO MOON-MOTHER. TWO LITTLE STARS
AGAIN GATHER THE BLUE TAFFETA AND WITH IT FORM A
CIRCLE AROUND MOON-MOTHER UPSTAGE LEFT. MOON-MOTHER
ENTERS STAGE LEFT. IF POSSIBLE, LIGHTS SHOULD FADE
DOWN WITH EXIT OF BIRDS AND FADE UP ON ENTRANCE OF
MOON-MOTHER.

SCENE FIVE

MOON-MOTHER   You are home early my sons. (SUSPICIOUS) What
has happened?

MORNING STAR   Scarface saved my life!

MOON-MOTHER   (STILL SUSPICIOUS) How so?

MORNING STAR   (PROUDLY) With my bow and arrows, he killed the
Black Birds.

MOON-MOTHER   (AFTER A PAUSE) Morning Star, you tried to shoot
the birds?

MORNING STAR   Yes.

MOON-MOTHER   (TO SCARFACE) You have earned your right,
Scarface. The Stars have moved and the Sun God can be told.

ACT THREE

LIGHTS TURN RED, THE BRIGHT LIGHT APPEARS AND DRUMS ARE HEARD. VOICE OFFSTAGE.

SUN GOD   Scarface, even while I slept I have seen what you have done. Ask of me what you came to ask and the Sun God will answer you.

SCARFACE   Moon-Mother, may I speak?

MOON-MOTHER   You may speak when the Sun God asks, but let my veil protect you.

SUN GOD   Speak, Scarface.

SCARFACE   (TREMBLING BEFORE THE LIGHT. HIS EYES CLOSED) Oh God of the Sun, I ask for Blue Water's hand in marriage. And if you consent, give me a sign to bring back to her. Heal this scar on my cheek by your light.

SUN GOD   (PAUSE) The Sun God consents because he treasures Blue Water. Turn in my light. Turn twice round.

(SCARFACE TURNS. REMOVES SCAR MADE OF PUTTY WHILE BACK IS TO AUDIENCE)

My light has healed. The sign is found. These two feathers I give to you from the Raven Birds you slew.

(OF COURSE, SCARFACE HAS HIDDEN THESE TWO FEATHERS UNDERNEATH HIS TUNIC. NOW HE REVEALS THEM)

You may wed Blue Water. Tell her this is my sign. The secret of healing is not only mine. You with your family will now begin what your tribe will call the House of Medicine. As I have healed, so shall you, with berries and herbs, seeds and skin. The medicine man uses heart and brain, both in the night and day. And if you must choose one or another, listen to what I say. Choose the brain - it never lies, but if you choose the heart, it may. (CHANGE OF TONE) Oh little Stars - open up the skies. Form the path of the Milky Way.

(LITTLE CHILDREN ENTER STAGE RIGHT AND STAGE LEFT AS STARS FORM A PATH)

Let him return to his people now. Let this end his stay.

END OF ACT TWO

SCENE ONE

SCENE AS IN ACT ONE. ADDED IS A LARGE RED SUN ON THE STAGE RIGHT BACKDROP. ALSO ADDED IS A LARGE CAULDRON NEAR THE STAGE LEFT FIRE. THE CAULDRON IS FILLED WITH FERMENTED JUICES WHICH ARE BEING SERVED TO THE VILL-AGERS AND THEIR NEIGHBOURING GUESTS. THE MOOD IS VERY

GAY AND FESTIVE. RED CLOUD IS SEATED NEAR HIS TENT IN A SEMI-CIRCLE WITH OTHER CHIEFS FROM OTHER TRIBES. HE IS SMOKING A PEACE PIPE AND PASSES IT ROUND TO THE OTHER CHIEFS. BLUE WATER IS SERVING THE JUICE FROM THE CAULDRON WHILE THE CROWD OF VISITORS AND VILL-AGERS MILL ABOUT. UPSTAGE RIGHT, HARDLY VISIBLE, IS A STRANGER WRAPPED IN A BLANKET OVER HIS HEAD AND BODY. HIS BACK IS TO THE AUDIENCE. HE IS ABSOLUTELY MOTIONLESS. KE-A-TAW IS HELPING BLUE WATER.

PLEASE NOTE THAT THROUGHOUT ACT THREE THE VILLAGERS ARE MOVING ABOUT CONSTANTLY, DRINKING, EATING AND CELEBRATING. THEY CAN BE DANCING OR PLAYING BUT MOV-EMENT SHOULD BE CONTINUOUS. THE CHIEFS AND ELDERS SHOULD BE SMOKING THE PEACE PIPE AND PASSING IT ON. ADLIB CONVERSATION SHOULD BE GOING ON CONTINUALLY, CONTROLLED WITH LOW VOICES WHEN SPECIFIC SCENES ARE BEING PLAYED.

DANCING BEAR   I see you're celebrating with the village, Blue Water. Do you think Scarface will return?

BLUE WATER   (HANDING HIM HIS DRINK) Yes. Scarface will return and enjoy this day of sharing our good fortune with our neighbouring tribes.

DANCING BEAR   Don't you ever give up hope?

BLUE WATER   No. I believe in a happy future.

DANCING BEAR   Why didn't you send me? I'd have returned by now.

BLUE WATER   Would you ask me to risk the life of our bravest warrior?

DANCING BEAR   Dancing Bear would have returned.

SINGING WIND SEES DANCING BEAR TALKING TO BLUE WATER. SHE GOES OVER TO HIM QUICKLY. SHE HOLDS ONE HAND BE-HIND HER BACK HIDING SOMETHING FROM VIEW.

SINGING WIND   (ANGRY) Who is your Squaw now? Blue Water or me?

DANCING BEAR   (APOLOGISING) I was only asking about Scarface.

SINGING WIND   (COMMANDING) You should talk to me. This is a celebration and celebrations are celebrated with the....

DANCING BEAR   (CHANGING THE SUBJECT) What do you have be-hind your back?

SINGING WIND   (FLIRTING) Something.

DANCING BEAR   For whom?

SINGING WIND   For – someone.

DANCING BEAR   Who is the someone?

SINGING WIND   Dancing Bear.

DANCING BEAR   What is it?

SINGING WIND   You'll see!

DANCING BEAR   Yes. I will!
> (GRABS SINGING WIND'S HAND QUICKLY AND PULLS FROM HER A WARRIOR CHIEF'S ROBE)

This is – for – me! Who gave this to you? (HE IS UPSET)

SINGING WIND   I made it.

DANCING BEAR   For me! Does Chief Red Cloud know, that you made a Chief's robe for me? (WORRIED)

SINGING WIND   No.

DANCING BEAR   Then, who told you to make this?

> KE–A–TAW HAS BEEN WATCHING THEM AND JOINS IN.

SINGING WIND   No one.

KE–A–TAW   Singing Wind – this can only bring trouble, because only a Chief may wear such a robe. You know that.

SINGING WIND   Of course I do. But who'll be our next chief?

DANCING BEAR   Yes, Old Mother, who'll be our next Chief? Shouldn't the greatest warrior of the Shawnees become the next chief?

SINGING WIND   When will Chief Red Cloud make up his mind? Today is the day to ask him – before the whole village.

KE–A–TAW   Wait, Singing Wind. Scarface may yet return.

SINGING WIND   How long are we to wait? Until it's too late?

DANCING BEAR   Old Squaw, what do you say to that?

KE–A–TAW   I say – wait – the answer will come.

> LITTLE ECHO IS WITH HER BROTHER GREY HAWK, CENTRE STAGE.

LITTLE ECHO   Why can't I have Laughing Face's moccasins? They're much too big for you!

GREY HAWK   And they'll fit you, my sister?

LITTLE ECHO   Of course not. I want to give them back to Laughing Face.

GREY HAWK   He can try to win them back.

LITTLE ECHO   You always pick on him.

GREY HAWK   You're old enough to sew him a new pair!

LITTLE ECHO   Just for that - I will.
> (RUNS AWAY STAGE LEFT AS GREY HAWK LAUGHS AFTER HER THEN TURNS AND GREETS A BRAVE FROM THE BLACKFEET)
Laughing Face - wait for me!

> SHE RUNS OVER TO HIM. HE IS GETTING SOMETHING TO DRINK FROM BLUE WATER.

LAUGHING FACE   Sh-h-h. Everyone will hear you. I'm not going anywhere.

LITTLE ECHO   Grey Hawk won't give me back your moccasins. So I'm going to make you a beautiful new pair.

LAUGHING FACE   Good enough to wear on the next Hunt?

LITTLE ECHO   They'll be the best in the whole village. (LAUGH-ING FACE LAUGHS) You'll see.

LAUGHING FACE   Who's that stranger sitting in the heat of the noon-day sun?

LITTLE ECHO   Where? I don't see anyone.

LAUGHING FACE   (POINTING UPSTAGE RIGHT) Over there!

LITTLE ECHO   Oh yes. He's so still. I thought it was a rock. How can anyone sit in the heat of such a sun and not be burned?

LAUGHING FACE   Maybe he's too shy to join us.

LITTLE ECHO   Let's invite him.

LAUGHING FACE   Why not?

LITTLE ECHO   Let's race.

> SHE RUNS STAGE RIGHT. LAUGHING FACE FOLLOWS. THEY REACH STRANGER TOGETHER.

LAUGHING FACE   Good afternoon. (SUDDENLY SHY) I mean - good noon - ah - welcome to our Village.

LITTLE ECHO   We can - see - you're - a - stranger. Would you like to join us in the celebrations of our Village?

STRANGER   You are kind to welcome a stranger.

LAUGHING FACE   But this celebration is to share the fruit of our land with strangers.

LITTLE ECHO   Why yes. Today all the neighbouring Chiefs are smoking the peace pipe. (GESTURES TOWARDS CHIEFS)

> STRANGER TAKES OFF BLANKET AND TURNS ROUND FACING THE AUDIENCE. IT IS A HANDSOME SCARFACE DRESSED MAGNIFICENTLY WITH THE COLOURS OF THE SUN. LAUGHING FACE AND LITTLE ECHO DON'T RECOGNISE HIM.

SCARFACE   Thank you both, I am honoured to share this day with you.

> THEY GO TO THE VILLAGE WHERE BLUE WATER IS SERVING STAGE LEFT. AS SCARFACE REACHES THE CAULDRON, HE SEES BLUE WATER. SHE RECOGNISES HIM. SHE STOPS SUDDENLY AND LOOKS AT HIM. THE WHOLE VILLAGE SEE SOMETHING HAS HAPPENED AND THEY TOO STAND STILL. THERE IS A SUDDEN SILENCE, EVEN CHIEF RED CLOUD REMAINS IMMOBILE.

BLUE WATER   Scarface! It is you.

SCARFACE   It is I, Blue Water. I have come back. (SMILES)

BLUE WATER   And the Sun God said 'yes'. I can see - by your face.

> CHIEF RED CLOUD CROSSES TO THEM.

SCARFACE   Chief Red Cloud, I ask now for Blue Water's hand in marriage.

RED CLOUD   My son, you have my consent. I doubted your return but feared to say so. My heart is full. Prepare now for the Wedding of Scarface and Blue Water.

DANCING BEAR   (AMAZED) He did return!

SINGING WIND   How do we know he saw the Sun God?

DANCING BEAR   Just look at his face. He has been there.

> THE VILLAGERS PREPARE BLUE WATER FOR THE WEDDING, DRESSING HER IN BRIDAL CLOTHES. THE MEN STAND BY SCARFACE. CHIEF RED CLOUD IN HIS JOY ANNOUNCES TO THE VILLAGE.

RED CLOUD   My people, one day I shall go to the Happy Hunting

Grounds and be with my Fathers. On that day Scarface will become your Chief and the Chief of the Hunt as well.

ALL   To Scarface!

SCARFACE   (TROUBLED) I thank you for such an honour, but I cannot be Chief of the Hunt.

> RED CLOUD AND THE WHOLE VILLAGE ARE STUNNED AND STOP THEIR ACTIVITY. EVERYONE LOOKS AT SCARFACE, NOT BE-LIEVING WHAT THEY HAVE JUST HEARD.

DANCING BEAR   All Shawnee Chiefs lead the Hunt. Is Scarface afraid?

GREY HAWK   We live by the Hunt!

LAUGHING FACE   Coward!

DANCING BEAR   I will not follow him!

BRAVES   Send him away!

> THEY START TO ADVANCE ON HIM. BLUE WATER HOLDS STILL AS SCARFACE STANDS BESIDE HER UNAFRAID. RED CLOUD HOLDS UP HIS HAND AND STOPS HIM.

RED CLOUD   Wait. Scarface must explain.

SCARFACE   (ANGERED) When I first came to this village, I brought three ears of corn, and you laughed at me. Now I have returned and brought these. (HOLDS UP TWO BLACK FEATHERS) Two black feathers from the Sun God and you are angry at me. It took strength to grow those few ears of corn in a barren valley. It took strength to bring back these raven wings which I earned from the Sun God. I will place them on my tent acc-ording to the Sun God's wishes. My tent will be known as a Medicine Lodge where I will heal the sick. I cannot kill and heal!

RED CLOUD   What is this Medicine tent or Lodge? It is unknown to us.

SCARFACE   The Sun God has given me the power to heal and my Lodge will be a House of Healing.

BLUE WATER   The Sun God gave you this secret?

SCARFACE   He has given me this gift, and it shall belong to the family of Scarface. So will it be with our sons, and their sons, and their son's sons, for all the moons to come.

RED CLOUD   Never before has there been a Medicine Man.

DANCING BEAR   But who will lead the Hunt?

SCARFACE Who is the greatest Shawnee Warrior?

ALL THE VILLAGE SHOUTS AND CHEERS.

ALL Dancing Bear is the greatest warrior!

RED CLOUD The decision is clear. Two Chiefs. Scarface - Dancing Bear you will both lead. Food and long life go hand in hand. (HE PUTS THEIR HANDS TOGETHER) The Hunter, Dancing Bear, must learn from the Healer; and the Healer, Scarface, must learn from the Hunter.

SINGING WIND BRINGS THE ROBE SHE MADE AND GIVES IT TO SCARFACE, AS HER TOKEN OF GOOD WILL. SCARFACE TAKES IT GENTLY FROM HER AND GIVES IT TO DANCING BEAR.

SCARFACE I already have the robes of the Chief Medicine Man which the Sun God gave me. Dancing Bear, I give you the Robe of Chief Hunter.

RED CLOUD Come join the Wedding of Blue Water and Scarface, and the coming of the Two Chiefs. Dance. Sing.

THE VILLAGE BEGIN TO DANCE IN GAY ABANDONMENT.

KE-A-TAW Let us return to the earth the richness it has given us. Life.

SHE AND MANY OF THE WOMEN POUR THE CONTENTS OF THE CAULDRON ON TO THE EARTH AS PART OF THE DANCE.

ALL (STILL DANCING) Life - life - long life.

ALL THE CHIEFS AND ELDERS EMPTY THEIR GOURDS ONTO THE EARTH. SCARFACE TAKES BLUE WATER'S HAND, AS THEY STAND CLOSE TOGETHER WHILE THE VILLAGE DANCES. THE VOICE OF THE SUN GOD IS HEARD TOWARD THE END OF THE DANCING. THE SOUNDS DIM AND HIS DIGNIFIED VOICE GROWS LOUDER.

SUN GOD (SLOWLY)
You may tell Blue Water
This is my sign
The secret of healing is not only mine.
As I have healed the scar on your cheek
So you will heal the scars of the weak.
You with your family will now begin
To build this new House of Medicine.

LIGHTS FADE SLOWLY UNTIL THERE IS DARKNESS ON STAGE.
CURTAIN.

END OF PLAY

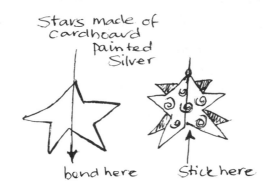

Stars made of
cardboard
painted
Silver

bend here

Stick here

backcloth is
Paper painted
or could be
Projections

Coloured
tissue
Paper
Stuck onto
logs with
mini hand fan
to blow tissue
like flames

tent is Paper
Painted + Suspended
by 3 bean poles
Macaroni shapes can
be stuck on

flat stone
made of
Papier mach
+ cardboard

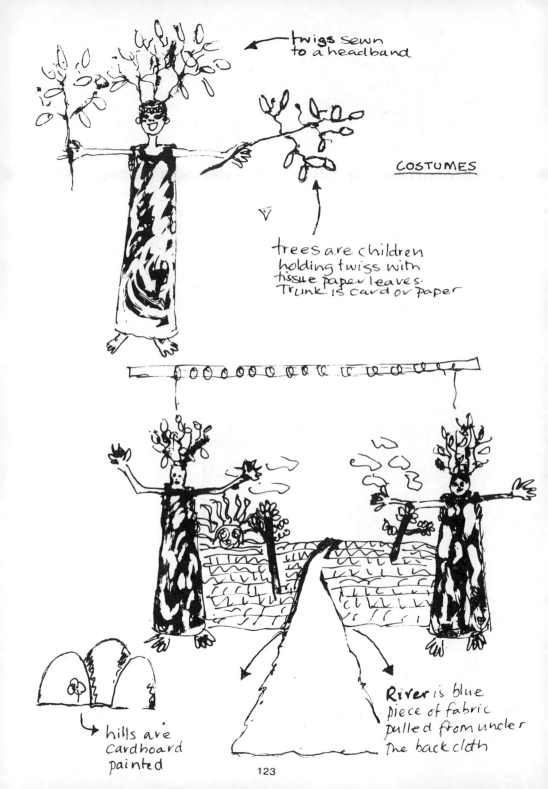

twigs sewn
to a headband

COSTUMES

trees are children
holding twigs with
tissue paper leaves.
Trunk is card or paper

hills are
cardboard
painted

River is blue
piece of fabric
pulled from under
the back cloth

123

Scarface's warshield
a cardboard circle
with feathers attached
and painted silver

Scarface's
War Jacket

Rope
straps

feather
decorations

LooRoles
stuckonto
a card-
board
breastplate

Chief Red Cloud's
Head-dress
made with a strip
of corrugated card
with feathers through
the holes

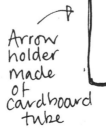

Arrow
holder
made
of
cardboard
tube

Arrows
made from
bean-poles
+ feathers
painted silver

124

COSTUMES

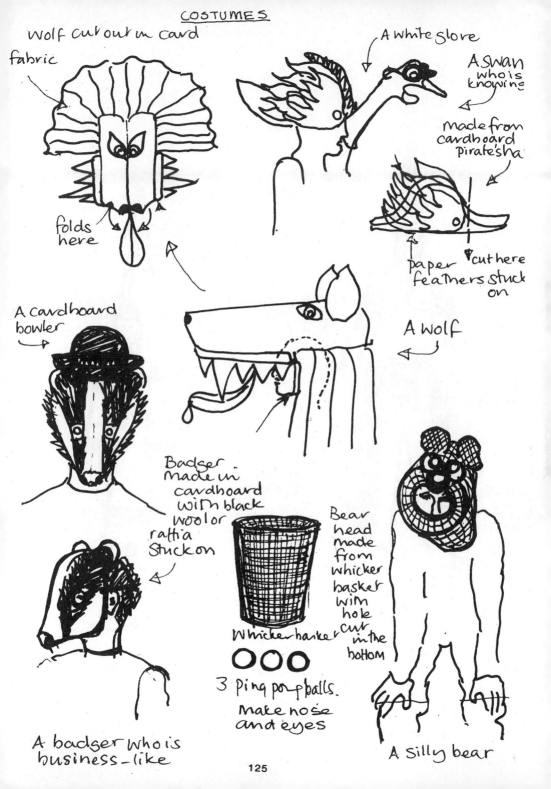

Wolf cut out in card

fabric

folds here

A white glove

A swan who is knowing

made from cardboard Pirate's ha

paper feathers stuck on

cut here

A cardboard bowler

A wolf

Badger made in cardboard with black wool or raffia stuck on

Bear head made from whicker basket with hole cut in the bottom

Whicker basket

3 ping pong balls. Make nose and eyes

A badger who is business-like

A silly bear

COSTUMES

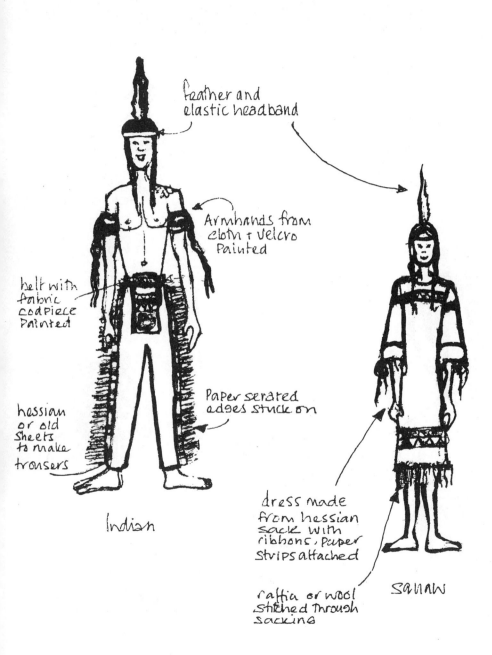

feather and
elastic headband

Armbands from
cloth + velcro
Painted

belt with
fabric
codpiece
Painted

hessian
or old
Sheets
to make
trousers

Paper serated
edges stuck on

Indian

dress made
from hessian
sack with
ribbons, paper
strips attached

raffia or wool
stitched through
sacking

SQUAW

COSTUMES

MAKE-UD FOR SQUAWS
AND SCARFACE

MADE FROM FLOWER DETALS AND LEAVES - DRESS FOR FEW HOURS
THEN ATTACH   WITH A LITTLE EGG   WHITE
                     SIMDLY WASH OFF

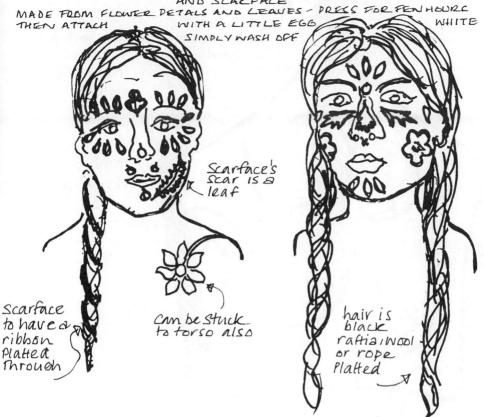

Scarface's
Scar is a
leaf

Can be stuck
to torso also

scarface
to have a
ribbon
Platted
Through

hair is
black
raftia wool
or rope
Platted

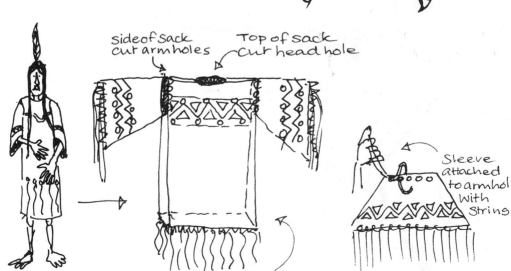

Side of sack
cut armholes

Top of sack
cut head hole

Sleeve
attached
to armhol
With
String

Boddice is a
Hessian sack

127

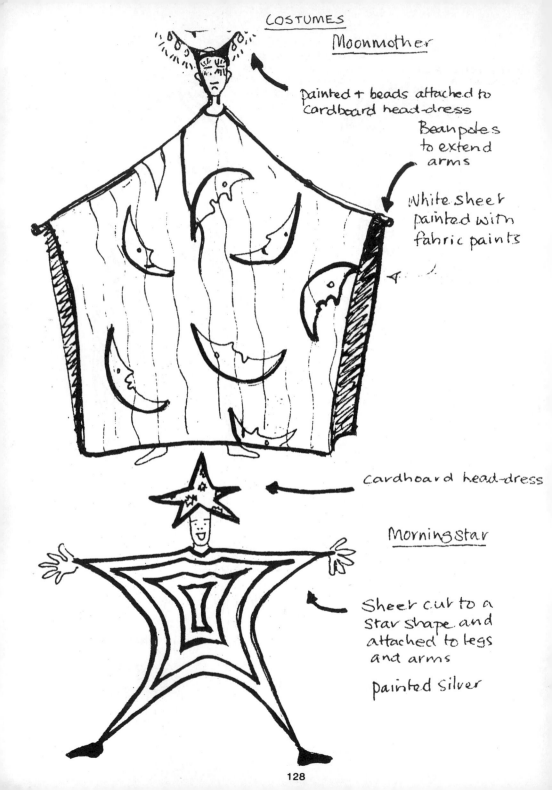

COSTUMES

Moonmother

Painted + beads attached to
Cardboard head-dress

Beanpoles
to extend
arms

White sheet
painted with
fabric paints

Cardboard head-dress

Morningstar

Sheet cut to a
star shape and
attached to legs
and arms

Painted silver

COSTUMES

Silver shield with feathers

Raven's feathers

Wigs of black wool stuck on a nylon stocking

hessian Sack dress

Silver arrows are bean poles with feathers attached

fringes are coloured wool or raffia

Hessian Sacking trousers frayed at sides

feathers attached to Slippers

Scarface and Blue water

PROPS FOR PIED PIPER

1. Large portable basket with handles.
2. Many hats of all description (Cook, Cobbler, Blacksmith etc)
3. Large roll of cloth with many holes in it.
4. The piper's flute or fife - any antique-looking reed instrument.
5. Large bell with long handle.
6. Cloaks of various colours. One cloak long and white.
7. 3 crowns - (King, Queen and the Stranger)
8. Floral wreaths.
9. Flowers strung together and a few single flowers.
10. Sword (King), large and ornate.
11. Magic scarves that turn from red to green and back again.

PROPS FOR THE FIRE BIRD

1. Fans for Princes.
2. 1 very large fan for the Empress. (Black and Gold)
3. 3 small saki cups (like very small Chinese tea cups)
4. Tray.
5. Wine jug.
6. 2 swords. (Oriental)
7. Bowl filled with red and pink paper flakes.
8. 2 Fire sticks for Firebird.

PROPS FOR INFANTA

1. 3 crowns. (King, Queen and Don Pedro)
2. Sword. (Don Pedro)
3. 2 Suitcases.
4. Large candle and candle-holder.
5. Doll dressed as Infanta.
6. Flowers. (Wreaths and single flowers)
7. Handkerchiefs. (Large and small, some red, mostly white)
8. Fan.